CAMPBELL IMAGE PRESENTATION LIBRARY
with VISUAL GUIDE

for the exclusive use of adopters of

Essential Biology

SECOND EDITION

and

Essential Biology
with Physiology

Campbell • Reece • Simon

PEARSON

Benjamin
Cummings

San Francisco Boston New York
Cape Town Hong Kong London Madrid Mexico City
Montreal Munich Paris Singapore Sydney Tokyo Toronto

Executive Editor: Beth Wilbur
Acquisitions Editor: Chalon Bridges
Editorial Project Manager: Ginnie Simione Jutson
Production Editor: Corinne Benson
Production Artist: Karl Miyajima
Developmental Editor: Evelyn Dahlgren
Senior Producer, Art and Media: Russell Chun
Publishing Assistant: Nora Lally-Graves
Managing Editor, Production: Erin Gregg
Senior Marketing Manager: Josh Frost
Compositor: The Left Coast Group

ISBN 0-8053-7498-1

PEARSON
Benjamin
Cummings

Benjamin Cummings
1301 Sansome Street
San Francisco, CA 94111
www.aw.com/bc

1 2 3 4 5 6 7 8 9 10—VHO—06 05 04 03

Preface

The *Campbell Image Presentation Library* is a chapter-by-chapter visual archive of more than 2,500 images for the exclusive use of adopters of *Essential Biology,* Second Edition and *Essential Biology with Physiology* by Campbell, Reece, and Simon. All of the diverse visual resources—art, tables, photos, videos, and animations—are organized by chapter. All file formats have been thoroughly tested in large lecture halls.

Contents

- More than **1,000 photos.** Includes all photos from the text plus additional photos collected from a variety of sources. The extra photos have been especially chosen to match the content of each chapter.
- All the **art and tables** from the text in .jpeg or .gif format. Art figures are provided with and without labels for maximum flexibility in your lecture presentations. Use the version without labels to customize the art for your lecture, create a quiz, or create step-by-step presentations. All of the art and tables have been reformatted to be larger and clearer when used for lecture presentation.
- **Layered art.** Selected art figures are layered for step-by-step presentation.
- **110 animations** to help students understand key biological concepts.
- **85 video clips.** Enhance your lectures with QuickTime videos on a variety of biological concepts. Scripts are provided for background information. Available in big (640 x 480) and small (320 x 240) formats.
- All visual resources in an easy-to-use viewer. Easily browse thumbnails and view enlarged images on screen so you can decide which images to use in lecture.

The *Campbell Image Presentation Library* is available on CD-ROM and in the Instructor Resources section of the Essential Biology Website.

Visual Guide

The *Visual Guide* provides:
- A "Getting Started" guide.
- Printed thumbnail-sized images for easy viewing of all resources.
- A complete photo list that also includes background information for the additional photos.
- A list of art and tables.
- Lists of the animations and suggested scripts for the videos.

These lists are also available in Word in the Documentation folder on the CD-ROMS.

Getting Started

The new Campbell Image Presentation Library is a chapter-by-chapter visual archive that includes more than 2,500 images—art, tables, photos, videos, and animations—provided in a user-friendly format. To get started, insert one of the CD-ROMs to view its contents as shown below:

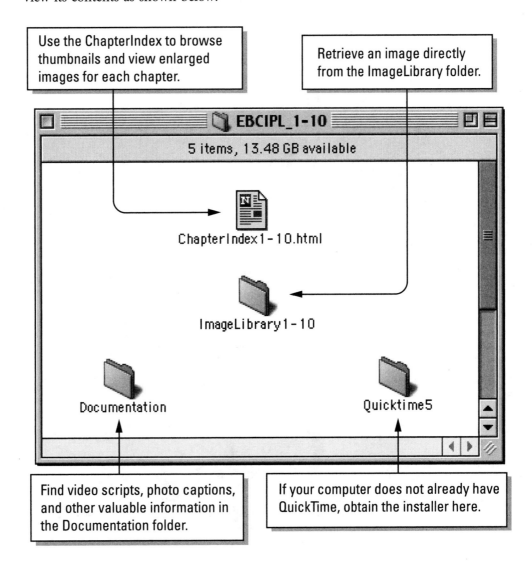

Use the ChapterIndex to browse thumbnails and view enlarged images for each chapter.

Retrieve an image directly from the ImageLibrary folder.

ChapterIndex1-10.html

ImageLibrary1-10

Documentation

Quicktime5

Find video scripts, photo captions, and other valuable information in the Documentation folder.

If your computer does not already have QuickTime, obtain the installer here.

Using the ChapterIndex.html file

The ChapterIndex.html file lets you easily browse the images available for each chapter. To access the images for a specific chapter, double-click the ChapterIndex.html file.

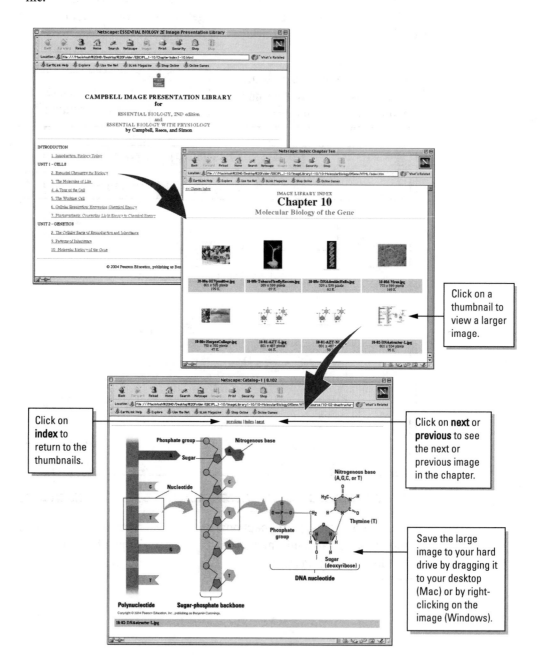

Click on a thumbnail to view a larger image.

Click on **index** to return to the thumbnails.

Click on **next** or **previous** to see the next or previous image in the chapter.

Save the large image to your hard drive by dragging it to your desktop (Mac) or by right-clicking on the image (Windows).

Using the ImageLibrary Folder

You may also retrieve the images in the Campbell Image Presentation Library by opening the ImageLibrary folder.

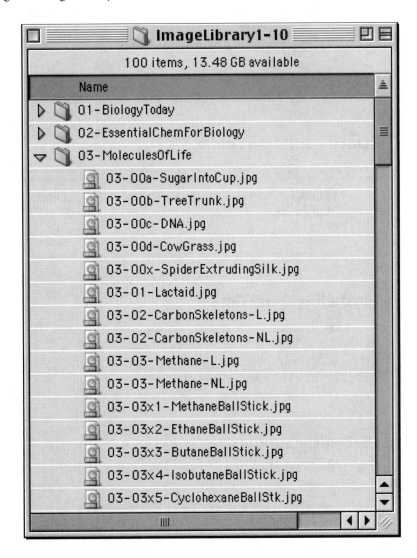

All images—art, tables, photos, videos, and animations—are organized by chapter and named according to their module number order. Double-click on an image to view it. If the image does not open, you may need to install QuickTime. If you are an adopter of *Essential Biology*, you may save an image to your hard drive by dragging it to your hard drive.

Key to File Name Codes

L	Art with labels
NL	Art without labels
L1, L2, etc.	Layers for step-by-step presentation of selected art figures
T	Table
B	Big-format video (640 x 480)
S	Small-format video (320 x 240)
x	Extra photo
UN	Unnumbered figure (with page number)

Documentation Folder

Highlights of the Documentation Folder include:

- Photo Captions file that provides a complete list of photos plus background information for the additional photos not found in the text.

- Video Scripts file that provides suggested scripts for the videos.

- Animations file that lists all available animations.

Installing QuickTime

Viewing the animations and videos requires QuickTime. For your convenience, QuickTime 5.0 is provided on each of the CD-ROMs. To install QuickTime on your computer, double-click the QuickTimeInstaller.exe file (Windows) or the QuickTime Installer file (Mac) and follow the directions that appear on screen. You may have to restart your computer after installation is complete.

Technical Support

For technical support, please visit www.aw.com/techsupport or send e-mail to media-support@pearsoned.com with a detailed description of your computer system and the technical problem. You can also call our tech support hotline at 1-800-677-6337, Monday–Friday, 8 A.M.–5 P.M. CST.

Pearson Education, Inc. License Agreement

for PowerPoint Lectures to accompany *Essential Biology,* Second Edition and *Essential Biology with Physiology,* by Neil A. Campbell, Jane B. Reece, and Eric J. Simon.

Please complete this License and mail it to Publishing Assistant, Biology, Benjamin Cummings/Pearson Education, Inc. 1301 Sansome Street, San Francisco, CA 94111.

Warning: Pearson Education, Inc., publishing as Benjamin Cummings, is willing to license to you the use of these CD-ROMs, only upon the condition that you accept all of the terms contained in this License by filling in the appropriate information and returning a signed print-out of the original license to the address provided. Please note: (1) there are two sections that require completion, (2) when completing the requested information, please use block lettering.

As an ADOPTER of ESSENTIAL BIOLOGY, Second Edition or ESSENTIAL BIOLOGY WITH PHYSIOLOGY, by Campbell, Reece, and Simon, © 2004 (THE "TEXTBOOK") for your course:

Title of your course: _____ ,
BENJAMIN/CUMMINGS, an imprint of PEARSON EDUCATION, INC., (LICENSOR) is pleased to grant

Your Name: _____

Located at:

Name of the Institution: _____

Street Address: _____

City/State/Zip Code: _____

("LICENSEE" OR "YOU") A ONE TIME, NON-ASSIGNABLE LICENSE TO USE THE **POWERPOINT LECTURES,** TO DISPLAY OR INCORPORATE THESE DIGITAL FILES INTO A COMPUTER-BASED TUTORIAL/LECTURE FOR THE CITED COURSE, TO INCLUDE THE DIGITAL FILES IN A PASSWORD-PROTECTED WEB SITE FOR THE CITED COURSE, AND TO CREATE STUDENT HANDOUTS FROM THE DIGITAL FILES FOR USE IN THE CITED COURSE, UNDER THE TERMS AND CONDITIONS OF THIS LICENSE AGREEMENT. THIS LICENSE IS CONTINGENT UPON YOUR ADOPTION OF THE TEXTBOOK FOR THE CITED COURSE AND WILL TERMINATE UPON PUBLICATION OF THE FIFTH EDITION OF THE WORK. THIS AGREEMENT BECOMES EFFECTIVE WHEN YOU MAIL A COMPLETED AND SIGNED COPY OF THIS LICENSE TO THE ADDRESS LISTED BELOW.

Ownership of the Product

1.   The digital files on this CD-ROM are owned by the Licensor and are protected by U.S. copyright laws, by laws of other nations, and by international treaties. If You violate any part of this Agreement, Your rights hereunder will terminate automatically. No notice shall be required from Licensor to effect such termination. In the event of termination, You must destroy all copies of the illustrations and all digital copies of the illustrations in Your possession and cease using same. Failure to destroy these copies upon termination of this License will result in a clear violation of U.S. copyright law.

Grant of License

2.   You may copy the digital files to a computer-based multimedia tutorial lecture program to support use of the Textbook in the Cited Course.

3.   You may copy the digital files from the Product to a web site, provided the site is password protected and accessible only to students registered for the Cited Course. You agree to inactivate the password at the end of each course term and to create a new password for each term of use.

4.   You may download and print out the digital files for the sole purpose of creating student handouts for use in the Cited Course.

Restrictions on Use

5.   Licensee agrees that the grant of this license is contingent upon its adoption of the Textbook for the Cited Course and upon satisfactory sales of the book for course use as determined by Licensor. Licensor reserves the right to terminate this agreement if it determines that sales of the Textbook decline as a result of this license or that the terms and conditions of this Agreement are not being fulfilled. In the event of termination You must destroy all printed copies of the files and all digital copies of the files in Your possession and cease using same.

6.   You may not create any derivative works, or alter or manipulate the illustrations, with the exception of labels, in any way.

7.   Credit will be given beneath each reproduced image regardless of format as follows: © Pearson Education, Inc., publishing as Benjamin Cummings.

8.   Full credit for reproduced illustrations and photographs are given in the Documentation folder on the PowerPoint Lectures CD-ROMs and are part of this Licensing Agreement.

Illustrations credited to Pearson Education have been borrowed from ESSENTIAL BIOLOGY, Second Edition/ESSENTIAL BIOLOGY WITH PHYSIOLOGY, by Campbell, Reece, and Simon, © 2004. These images have been produced from the originals by permission of the publisher. These illustrations may not be reproduced in any format for any purpose without express written permission from the publisher.

9.   You may not sub-license, sell, lend or lease the digital files or copies of the images, or derive any monetary compensation from usage of the digital files or copies of the images.

10. You may use the digital files and copies of the images for non-profit educational purposes for the Cited Course only.

11. All other rights are reserved by Licensor Limitations.

12. Licensor makes no warranty, express or implied, with respect to the creation, distribution, or use of the digital files. IN NO EVENT WILL LICENSOR BE LIABLE TO YOU FOR DAMAGES, INCLUDING ANY LOSS OF PROFITS, LOST SAVINGS, OR OTHER INCIDENTAL OR CONSEQUENTIAL DAMAGES ARISING OUT OF YOUR USE OR INABILITY TO USE THE DIGITAL FILES. Because some states do not allow for exclusion or limitation of liability for consequential or incidental damages, the above limitation may not apply to You.

13. The construction and performance of this Agreement will be governed by the internal, substantive laws of the State of California without regard for its choice of law rules.

POWERPOINT LECTURES for ESSENTIAL BIOLOGY, Second Edition or ESSENTIAL BIOLOGY WITH PHYSIOLOGY, by Neil A. Campbell, Jane B. Reece, and Eric J. Simon, © 2004 by Pearson Education, Inc., publishing as Benjamin Cummings.

All Companies' Rights Reserved.
Pearson Education, Inc.

Accepted and agreed by: _____

Name of your university or college: _____

Your name: _____

Title: _____

E-mail Address: _____

Date (MM/DD/YY): _____

Mail completed and signed copy to:

Publishing Assistant, Biology
Benjamin Cummings/Pearson Education, Inc.
1301 Sansome Street
San Francisco, California 94111

Contents

Chapter 1 Introduction: Biology Today

01-00a-Fungi.jpg

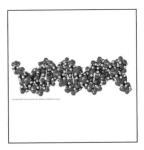

01-00b-DNAMolecule.jpg

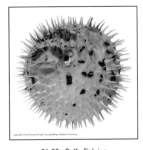

01-00c-PufferFish.jpg

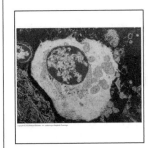

01-00d-EukcaryoticCell-L.jpg

01-01a-BioInTheNews.jpg

01-01b-BioInTheNews.jpg

01-01c-BioInTheNews.jpg

01-01d-BioInTheNews.jpg

01-01e-BioInTheNews.jpg

01-01f-BioInTheNews.jpg

01-01g-BioInTheNews.jpg

01-02a-Earth.jpg

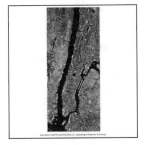

01-02b-CentralPark.jpg

01-02c-ParkWoodland.jpg

01-02d-Squirrel.jpg

01-02e-Cell-L.jpg

01-02e-Cell-NL.jpg

01-02f-DNA.jpg

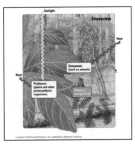

01-03-EcosysEnergyFlow-L.jpg

01-03-EcosysEnergyFlow-NL.jpg

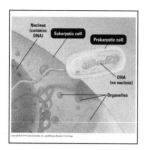

01-04-ProVsEucaryotic-L.jpg

01-04-ProVsEucaryotic-NL.jpg

01-05-DNAnucleotides.jpg

01-06-DNAbiotechnology.jpg

01-07-Diversity.jpg

01-08-DomainsKingdoms-L.jpg

01-08-DomainsKingdoms-NL.jpg

01-08a-DomainBacteria.jpg

01-08b-DomainArchaea.jpg

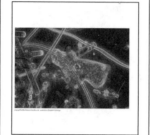

01-08c-KingdomProtista.jpg

01-08d-KingdomPlantae.jpg

01-08e-KingdomFungi.jpg

01-08f-KingdomAnimalia.jpg

01-09-UnityDiversity-L.jpg

01-09-UnityDiversity-NL.jpg

01-10-DinosaurFossil.jpg

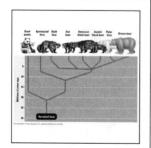

01-11-BearPhylogeny-L.jpg

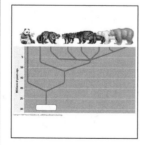

01-11-BearPhylogeny-NL.jpg

01-12-Darwin.jpg

01-12x-OriginOfSpecies.jpg

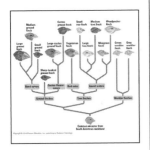

01-13-DarwinsFinches-L.jpg

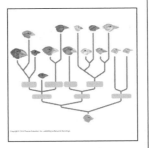

01-13-DarwinsFinches-NL.jpg

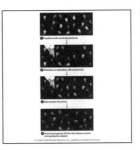

01-14-NaturalSelection-L.jpg

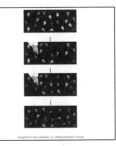

01-14-NaturalSelection-NL.jpg

01-14-SeaHorsesVideo-B.mov

01-14-SeaHorsesVideo-S.mov

01-15a-ArtificialSelect.jpg

01-15b-ArtificialSelect.jpg

01-16-ChestXray.jpg

01-17-EloyRodriguez.jpg

01-18-L1-ScientificMethod-L.jpg

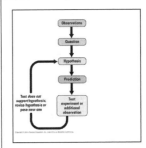

01-18-L2-ScientificMethod-L.jpg

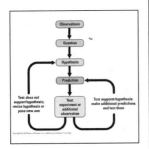

01-18-L3-ScientificMethod-L.jpg

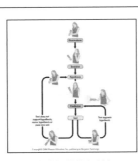

01-19-ScientificMethod-L.jpg

01-19-ScientificMethod-NL.jpg

01-20-SnakeMimicry-L.jpg

01-20-SnakeMimicry-NL.jpg

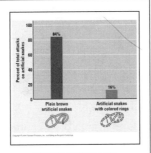

01-21-HypTestMimicry.jpg

01-22-ScienceSocial.jpg

01-23-DNAfingerprinting.jpg

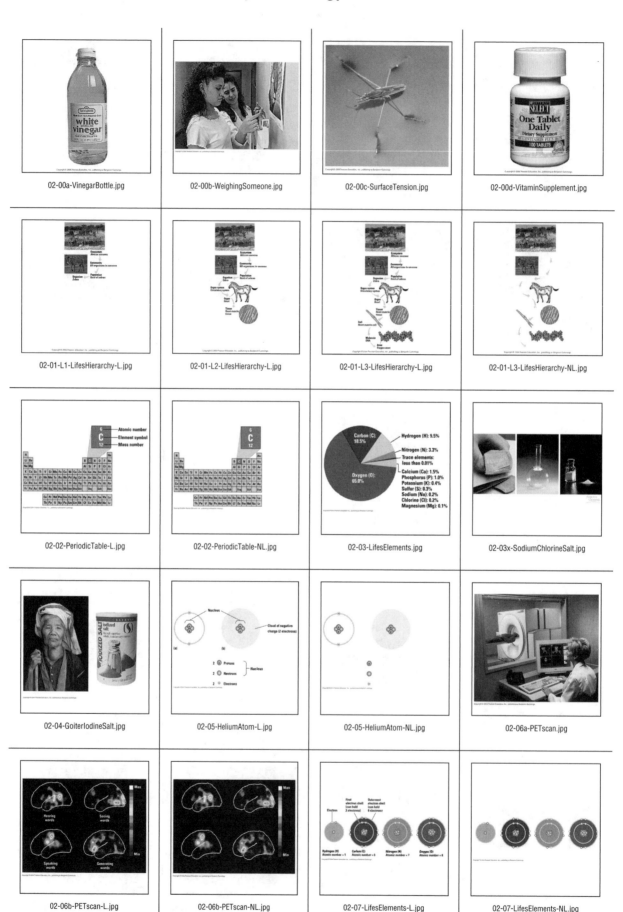

02-00a-VinegarBottle.jpg

02-00b-WeighingSomeone.jpg

02-00c-SurfaceTension.jpg

02-00d-VitaminSupplement.jpg

02-01-L1-LifesHierarchy-L.jpg

02-01-L2-LifesHierarchy-L.jpg

02-01-L3-LifesHierarchy-L.jpg

02-01-L3-LifesHierarchy-NL.jpg

02-02-PeriodicTable-L.jpg

02-02-PeriodicTable-NL.jpg

02-03-LifesElements.jpg

02-03x-SodiumChlorineSalt.jpg

02-04-GoiterIodineSalt.jpg

02-05-HeliumAtom-L.jpg

02-05-HeliumAtom-NL.jpg

02-06a-PETscan.jpg

02-06b-PETscan-L.jpg

02-06b-PETscan-NL.jpg

02-07-LifesElements-L.jpg

02-07-LifesElements-NL.jpg

02-07bx-SaltCrystalPhoto.jpg

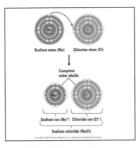

02-08-IonicBondFormation-L.jpg

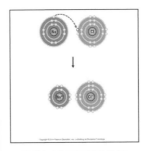

02-08-IonicBondFormation-NL.jpg

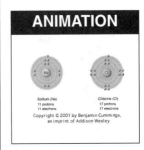

02-08-IonicBondsAnim.mov

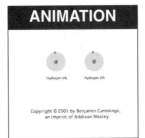

02-08x-MethaneBallStick.jpg

02-09-CovalentBondsAnim.mov

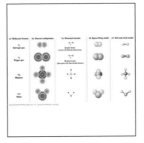

02-09-MoleculeRepresent.jpg

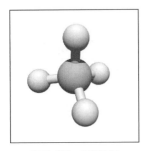

02-10-EarthWaterWorld.jpg

02-10x-Earth.gif

02-10x-WaterCollage.jpg

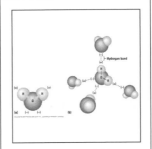

02-11-PolarMolecule-L.jpg

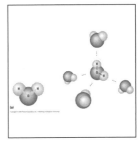

02-11-PolarMolecule-NL.jpg

02-12-Cohesion-L.jpg

02-12-Cohesion-NL.jpg

02-12x-TreesCohesionOfWater.jpg

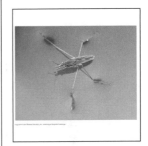

02-13-SurfaceTension.jpg

02-13x1-IceFishing.jpg

02-13x2-FrozenWaterBenzene.jpg

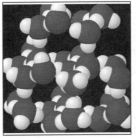

02-13x3-IceMolecularModel.gif

02-13x4-WaterMolecularModel.gif

02-14-EvaporativeCooling.jpg

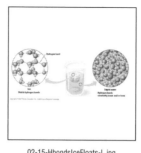

02-15-HbondsIceFloats-L.jpg

02-15-HbondsIceFloats-NL.jpg

02-16-SaltInWater-L.jpg

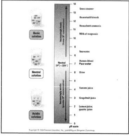

02-16-SaltInWater-NL.jpg

02-17-pHscale-L.jpg

02-17-pHscale-NL.jpg

02-18-FxAcidRainTrees.jpg

02-18x1-AcidRainTreeDamage.jpg

02-18x2-Smokestacks.jpg

02-19-Volcanism.jpg

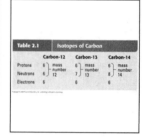

02-T01-CarbonIsotopes.jpg

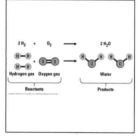

02-UNp27-ChemicalReact-L.jpg

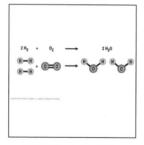

02-UNp27-ChemicalReact-NL.jpg

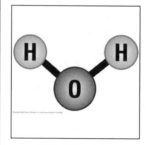

02-UNp28-Water-L.jpg

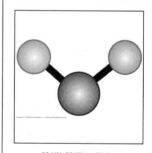

02-UNp28-Water-NL.jpg

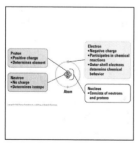

02-VS01-AtomicStructur-L.jpg

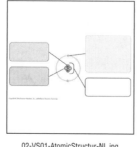

02-VS01-AtomicStructur-NL.jpg

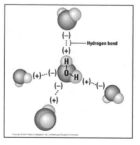

02-VS02-HydrogenBonds-L.jpg

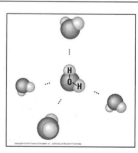

02-VS02-HydrogenBonds-NL.jpg

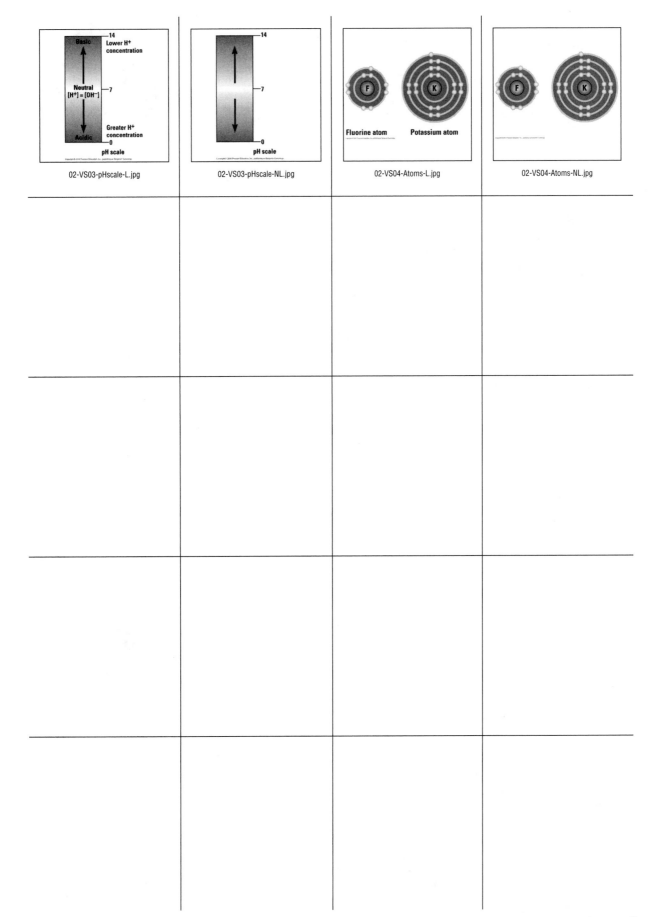

02-VS03-pHscale-L.jpg

02-VS03-pHscale-NL.jpg

02-VS04-Atoms-L.jpg

02-VS04-Atoms-NL.jpg

Chapter 3 The Molecules of Life

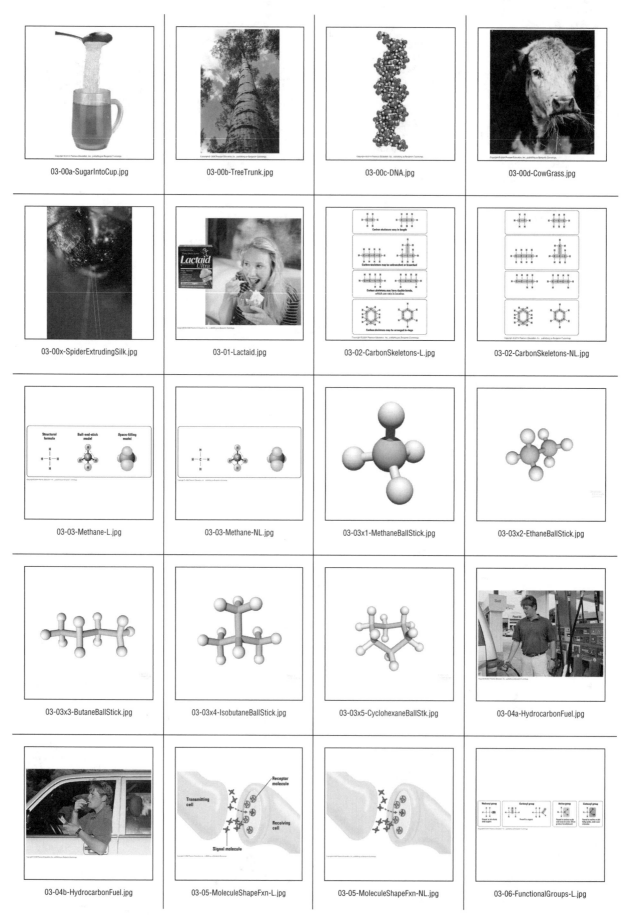

03-00a-SugarIntoCup.jpg

03-00b-TreeTrunk.jpg

03-00c-DNA.jpg

03-00d-CowGrass.jpg

03-00x-SpiderExtrudingSilk.jpg

03-01-Lactaid.jpg

03-02-CarbonSkeletons-L.jpg

03-02-CarbonSkeletons-NL.jpg

03-03-Methane-L.jpg

03-03-Methane-NL.jpg

03-03x1-MethaneBallStick.jpg

03-03x2-EthaneBallStick.jpg

03-03x3-ButaneBallStick.jpg

03-03x4-IsobutaneBallStick.jpg

03-03x5-CyclohexaneBallStk.jpg

03-04a-HydrocarbonFuel.jpg

03-04b-HydrocarbonFuel.jpg

03-05-MoleculeShapeFxn-L.jpg

03-05-MoleculeShapeFxn-NL.jpg

03-06-FunctionalGroups-L.jpg

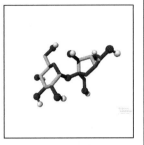

03-06-FunctionalGroups-NL.jpg

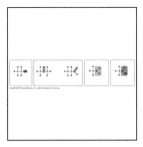

03-06x3-SucroseBallStick.jpg

03-07-MacromoleculesAnim.mov

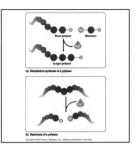

03-07-SynthHydrolysis-L.jpg

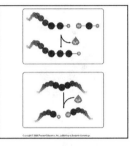

03-07-SynthHydrolysis-NL.jpg

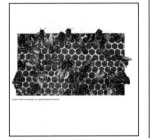

03-08-BeeHoney.jpg

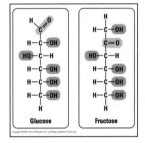

03-09-MonosacchIsomers-L.jpg

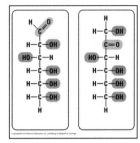

03-09-MonosacchIsomers-NL.jpg

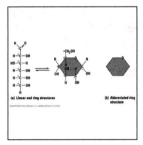

03-10-GlucoseStructure-L.jpg

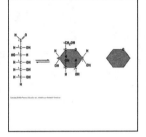

03-10-GlucoseStructure-NL.jpg

03-10x-GlucoseBallStick.jpg

03-11-DisaccharidesAnim.mov

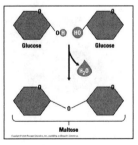

03-11-DisaccharideSynth-L.jpg

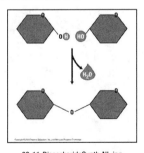

03-11-DisaccharideSynth-NL.jpg

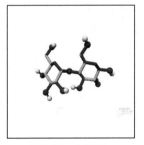

03-11x-MaltoseBallStick.jpg

03-12-DietarySugar.jpg

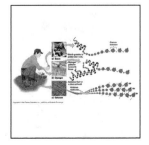

03-13-Polysaccharides-L.jpg

03-13-Polysaccharides-NL.jpg

03-13-PolysaccharidesAnim.mov

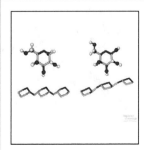

03-13x-StarchCellulose.jpg

03-14-Symbiosis.jpg

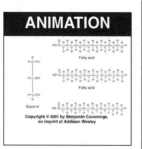

03-15-FatsAnim.mov

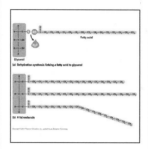

03-15-FatSynthesis-L.jpg

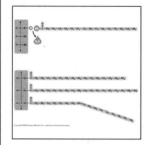

03-15-FatSynthesis-NL.jpg

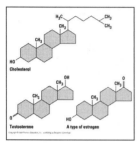

03-16-Steroids-L.jpg

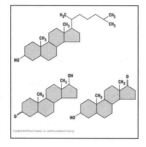

03-16-Steroids-NL.jpg

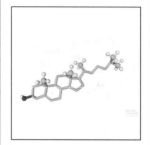

03-16x-CholesterolBallStk.jpg

03-17-SteroidMuscle.jpg

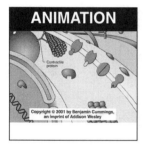

03-18-ContractProteinsAnim.mov

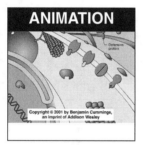

03-18-DefensiveProteinsAnim.mov

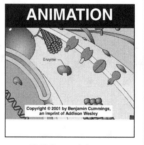

03-18-EnzymesAnim.mov

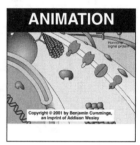

03-18-SignalProteinsAnim.mov

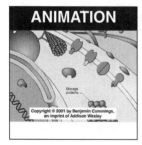

03-18-StorageProteinsAnim.mov

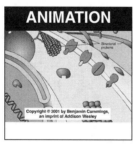

03-18-StructuralProtAnim.mov

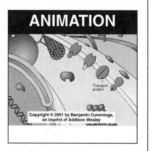

03-18-TransportProtAnim.mov

03-18a-StructuralProtein.jpg

03-18b-StorageProtein.jpg

03-18c-ContractileProtein.jpg

03-18d-TransportProtein.jpg

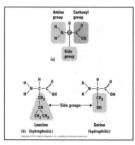

03-19-AminoAcidStructur-L.jpg

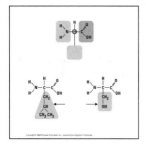

03-19-AminoAcidStructur-NL.jpg

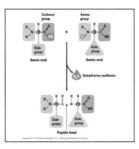

03-20-JoinAminoAcid-L.jpg

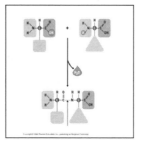

03-20-JoinAminoAcid-NL.jpg

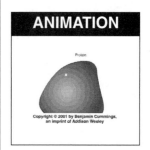

03-21-ProteinStructureAnim.mov

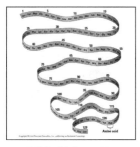

03-21-ProtPrimStructur-L.jpg

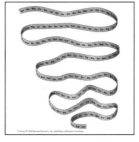

03-21-ProtPrimStructur-NL.jpg

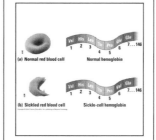

03-22-SickleCellHb-L.jpg

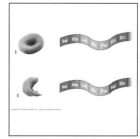

03-22-SickleCellHb-NL.jpg

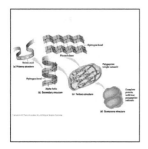

03-23-ProteinStructure-L.jpg

03-23-ProteinStructure-NL.jpg

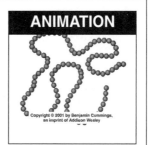

03-23a-PrimaryStructureAnim.mov

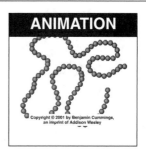

03-23b-SecondStructureAnim.mov

03-23c-TertStructureAnim.mov

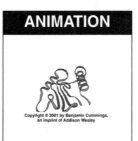

03-23d-QuatStructureAnim.mov

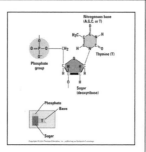

03-24-DNAnucleotides-L.jpg

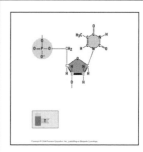

03-24-DNAnucleotides-NL.jpg

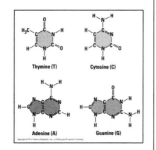

03-25-DNAnucleotides-L.jpg

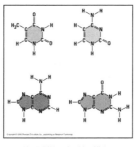

03-25-DNAnucleotides-NL.jpg

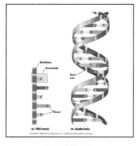

03-26-DNA-L.jpg

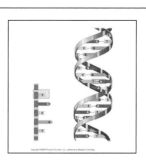

03-26-DNA-NL.jpg

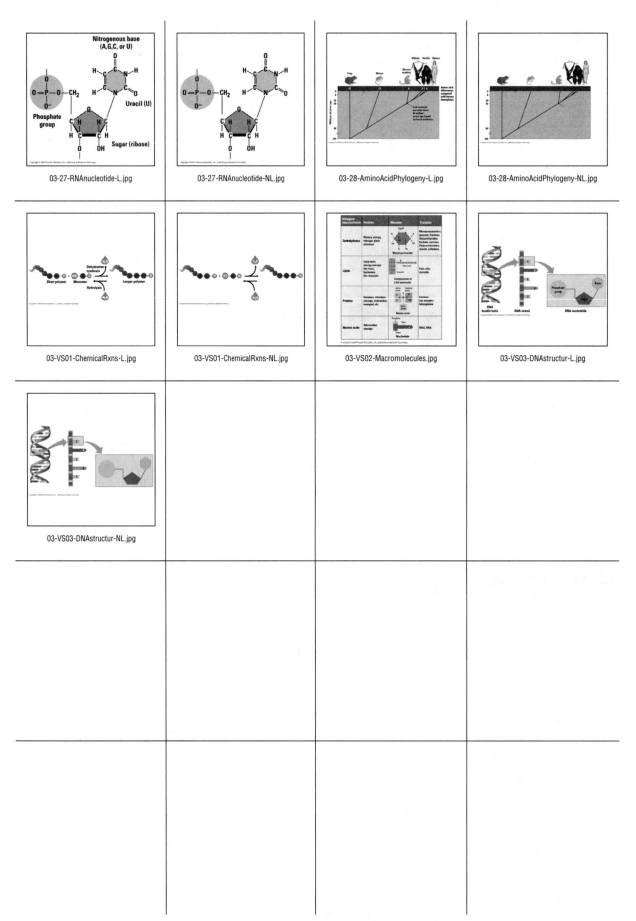

03-27-RNAnucleotide-L.jpg

03-27-RNAnucleotide-NL.jpg

03-28-AminoAcidPhylogeny-L.jpg

03-28-AminoAcidPhylogeny-NL.jpg

03-VS01-ChemicalRxns-L.jpg

03-VS01-ChemicalRxns-NL.jpg

03-VS02-Macromolecules.jpg

03-VS03-DNAstructur-L.jpg

03-VS03-DNAstructur-NL.jpg

Chapter 4 A Tour of the Cell

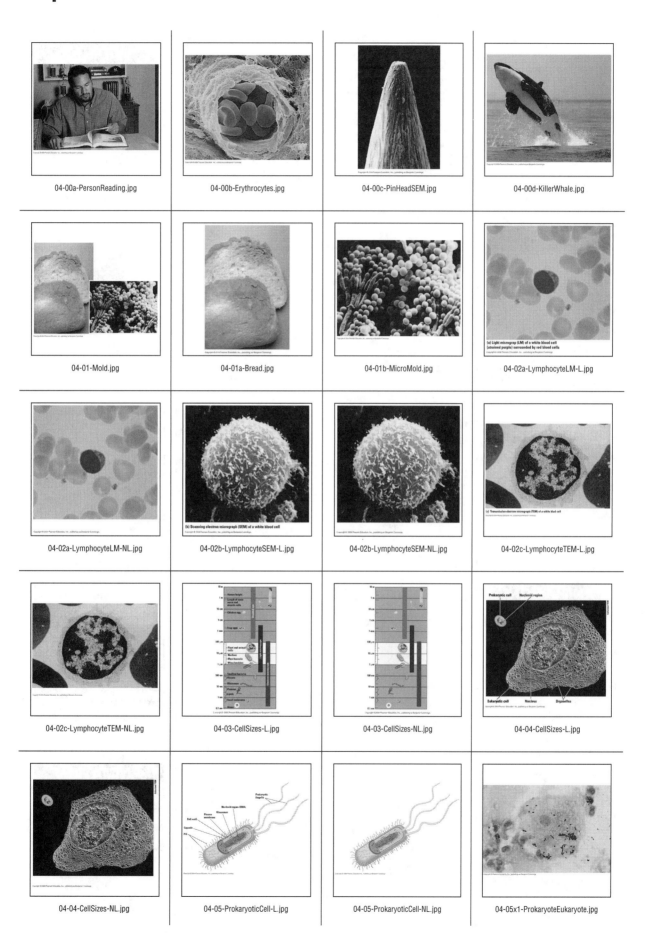

04-00a-PersonReading.jpg

04-00b-Erythrocytes.jpg

04-00c-PinHeadSEM.jpg

04-00d-KillerWhale.jpg

04-01-Mold.jpg

04-01a-Bread.jpg

04-01b-MicroMold.jpg

04-02a-LymphocyteLM-L.jpg

04-02a-LymphocyteLM-NL.jpg

04-02b-LymphocyteSEM-L.jpg

04-02b-LymphocyteSEM-NL.jpg

04-02c-LymphocyteTEM-L.jpg

04-02c-LymphocyteTEM-NL.jpg

04-03-CellSizes-L.jpg

04-03-CellSizes-NL.jpg

04-04-CellSizes-L.jpg

04-04-CellSizes-NL.jpg

04-05-ProkaryoticCell-L.jpg

04-05-ProkaryoticCell-NL.jpg

04-05x1-ProkaryoteEukaryote.jpg

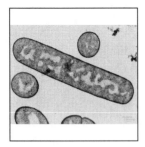

04-05x2-BacillusPolymyxa.jpg

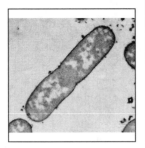

04-05x3-Ecoli.jpg

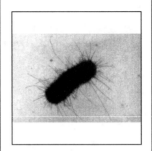

04-05x4-Pili.jpg

04-06-CytoplasmStreVideo-B.mov

04-06-CytoplasmStreVideo-S.mov

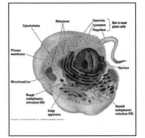

04-06a-AnimalCell-L.jpg

04-06a-AnimalCell-NL.jpg

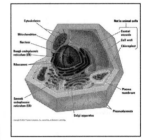

04-06b-PlantCell-L.jpg

04-06b-PlantCell-NL.jpg

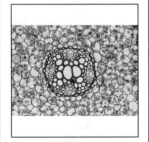

04-06bx-PlantCells.jpg

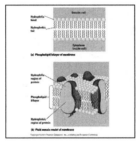

04-07-PlasmaMembrane-L.jpg

04-07-PlasmaMembrane-NL.jpg

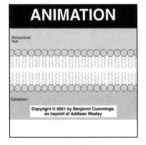

04-07a-MembraneStructure.mov

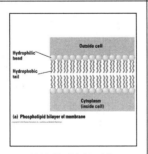

04-07a-PhosBylayMem-L.jpg

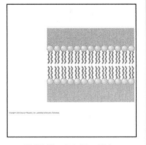

04-07a-PhosBylayMem-NL.jpg

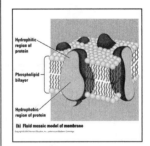

04-07b-FluiMosaModel-L.jpg

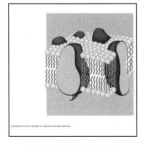

04-07b-FluiMosaModel-NL.jpg

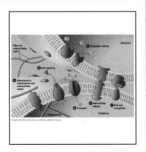

04-08-MembraneProteinFxn-L.jpg

04-08-MembraneProteinFxn-NL.jpg

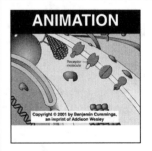

04-08-ReceptorProtAnim.mov

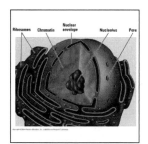

04-09-Nucleus-L.jpg

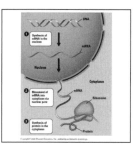

04-09-Nucleus-NL.jpg

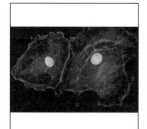

04-09x-Nuclei.jpg

04-10-NucleusFxn-L.jpg

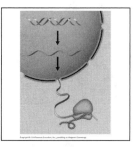

04-10-NucleusFxn-NL.jpg

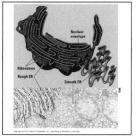

04-11-ER-L.jpg

04-11-ER-NL.jpg

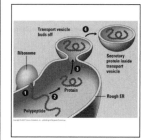

04-12-rERfxn-L.jpg

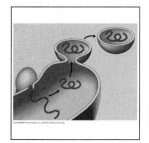

04-12-rERfxn-NL.jpg

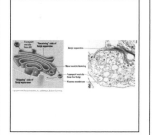

04-13-GolgiApparatus-L.jpg

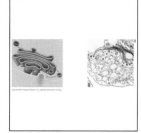

04-13-GolgiApparatus-NL.jpg

ANIMATION

Copyright © 2001 by Benjamin Cummings,
an imprint of Addison Wesley

04-14-LysosomeFormAnim.mov

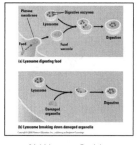

04-14-LysosomeFxn-L.jpg

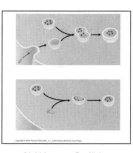

04-14-LysosomeFxn-NL.jpg

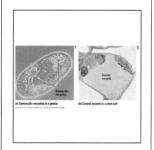

04-15-Vacuoles-L.jpg

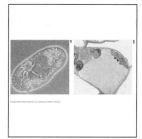

04-15-Vacuoles-NL.jpg

VIDEO

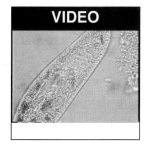

04-15A-ParameVacVideo-B.mov

VIDEO

04-15A-ParameVacVideo-S.mov

ANIMATION

Copyright © 2001 by Benjamin Cummings,
an imprint of Addison Wesley

04-16-EndomembraneSysAnim.mov

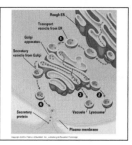

04-16-EndomembraneSystem-L.jpg

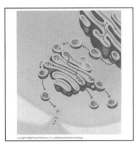

04-16-EndomembraneSystem-NL.jpg

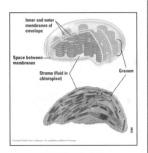

04-17-Chloroplast-L.jpg

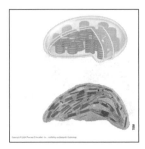

04-17-Chloroplast-NL.jpg

04-17x-Chloroplasts.jpg

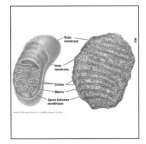

04-18-Mitochondrion-L.jpg

04-18-Mitochondrion-NL.jpg

04-19-Cytoskeleton-L.jpg

04-19-Cytoskeleton-NL.jpg

04-19a-Microtubules-L.jpg

04-19a-Microtubules-NL.jpg

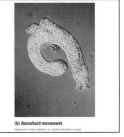

04-19b-AmoeboidMove-L.jpg

04-19b-AmoeboidMove-NL.jpg

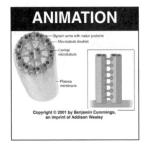

04-20-CiliaFlagellaAnim.mov

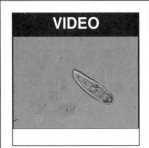

04-20-ParamecCiliaVideo-B.mov

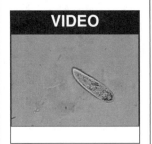

04-20-ParamecCiliaVideo-S.mov

04-20-SpermFlagellaCilia-L.jpg

04-20-SpermFlagellaCilia-NL.jpg

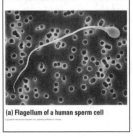

04-20a-Sperm-L.jpg

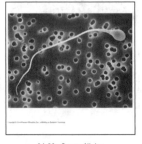

04-20a-Sperm-NL.jpg

04-20b-ProtistCilia-L.jpg

04-20b-ProtistCilia-NL.jpg

(c) Cilia lining the respiratory tract

04-20c-Cilia-L.jpg

04-20c-Cilia-NL.jpg

04-20x-Flagella.jpg

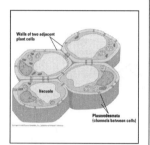

04-21-Plasmodesmata-L.jpg

04-21-Plasmodesmata-NL.jpg

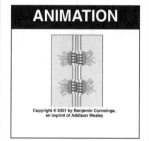

04-22-AnchorJunctionsAnim.mov

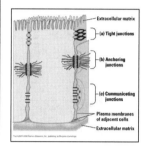

04-22-CellJunctions-L.jpg

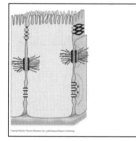

04-22-CellJunctions-NL.jpg

04-22-CommJunctionsAnim.mov

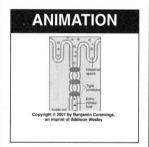

04-22-TightJunctionsAnim.mov

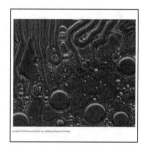

04-23-MembraneSelfAssembl.jpg

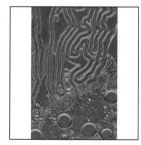

04-23x-PhospholipidSpheres.jpg

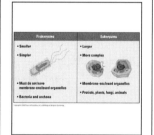

04-VS01-ProVsEukaryote.jpg

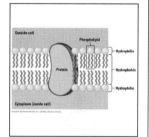

04-VS02-MembraneStructur-L.jpg

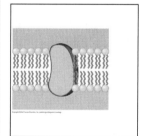

04-VS02-MembraneStructur-NL.jpg

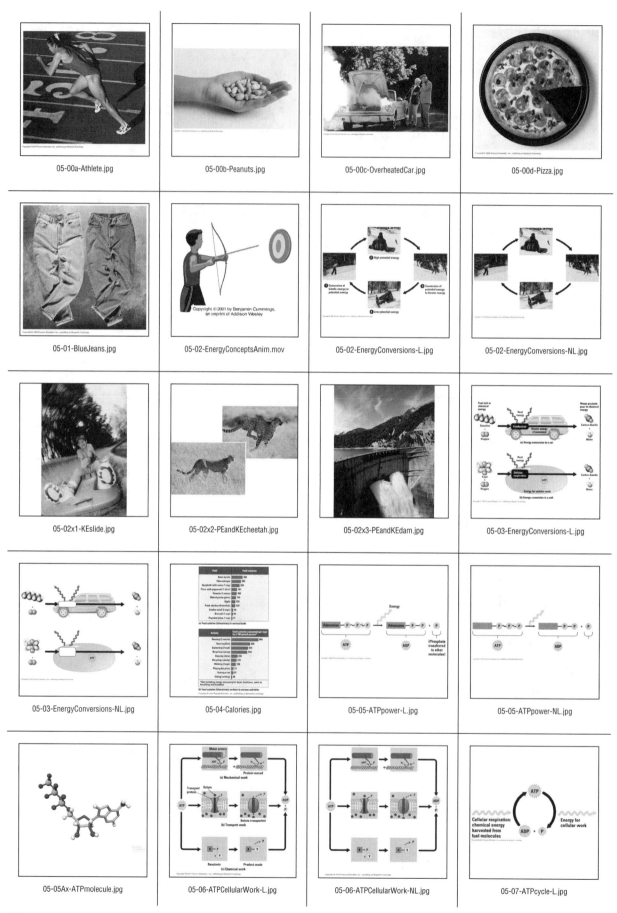

05-00a-Athlete.jpg

05-00b-Peanuts.jpg

05-00c-OverheatedCar.jpg

05-00d-Pizza.jpg

05-01-BlueJeans.jpg

05-02-EnergyConceptsAnim.mov

05-02-EnergyConversions-L.jpg

05-02-EnergyConversions-NL.jpg

05-02x1-KEslide.jpg

05-02x2-PEandKEcheetah.jpg

05-02x3-PEandKEdam.jpg

05-03-EnergyConversions-L.jpg

05-03-EnergyConversions-NL.jpg

05-04-Calories.jpg

05-05-ATPpower-L.jpg

05-05-ATPpower-NL.jpg

05-05Ax-ATPmolecule.jpg

05-06-ATPCellularWork-L.jpg

05-06-ATPCellularWork-NL.jpg

05-07-ATPcycle-L.jpg

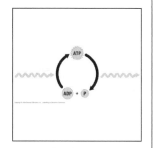

05-07-ATPcycle-NL.jpg

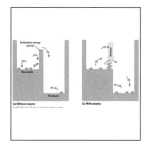

05-08-ActivationEnergy-L.jpg

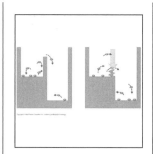

05-08-ActivationEnergy-NL.jpg

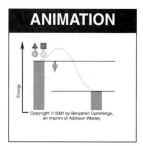

05-09-HowEnzymesWorkAnim.mov

05-09-L1-EnzymeFxn-L.jpg

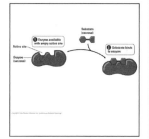

05-09-L2-EnzymeFxn-L.jpg

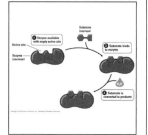

05-09-L3-EnzymeFxn-L.jpg

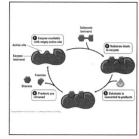

05-09-L4-EnzymeFxn-L.jpg

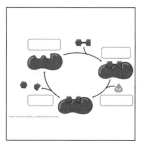

05-09-L4-EnzymeFxn-NL.jpg

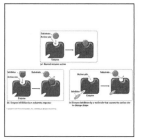

05-10-EnzymeInhibition-L.jpg

05-10-EnzymeInhibition-NL.jpg

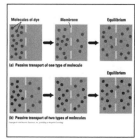

05-11-Diffusion-L.jpg

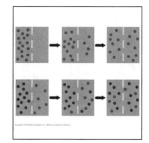

05-11-Diffusion-NL.jpg

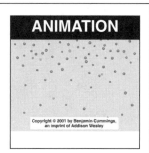

05-11-DiffusionAnim.mov

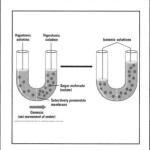

05-12-Osmosis-L.jpg

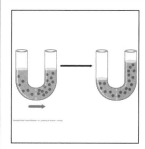

05-12-Osmosis-NL.jpg

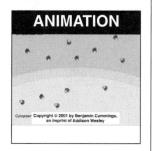

05-12-OsmosisAnim.mov

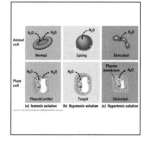

05-13-OsmoticEnvironment-L.jpg

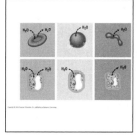

05-13-OsmoticEnvironment-NL.jpg

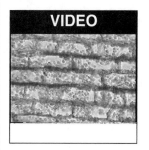

05-13-PlasmoElodeaVideo-B.mov

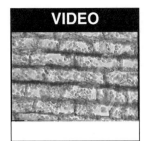

05-13-PlasmoElodeaVideo-S.mov

05-13-TurgidElodeaVideo-B.mov

05-13-TurgidElodeaVideo-S.mov

05-14-FlacidPlant.jpg

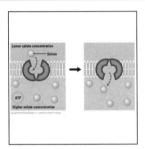

05-15-ActiveTransport-L.jpg

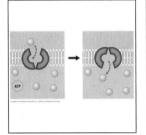

05-15-ActiveTransport-NL.jpg

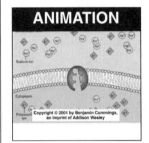

05-15-ActiveTransportAnim.mov

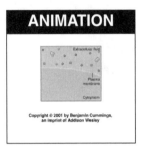

05-16-ExocytEndoIntroAnim.mov

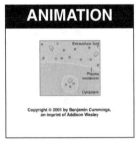

05-16-ExocytosisAnim.mov

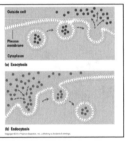

05-16-ExoEndocytosis-L.jpg

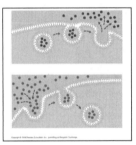

05-16-ExoEndocytosis-NL.jpg

05-17-Phagocytosis-L.jpg

05-17-Phagocytosis-NL.jpg

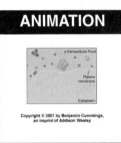

05-17-PhagocytosisAnim.mov

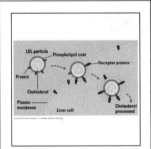

05-18-CholesterolUptake-L.jpg

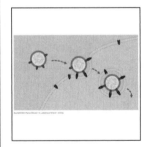

05-18-CholesterolUptake-NL.jpg

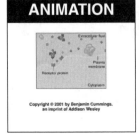

05-18-ReceptMedEndoAnim.mov

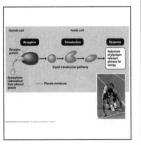

05-19-CellSignaling-L.jpg

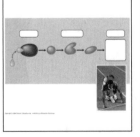

05-19-CellSignaling-NL.jpg

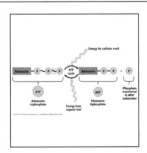

05-VS01-ATPCycle-L.jpg

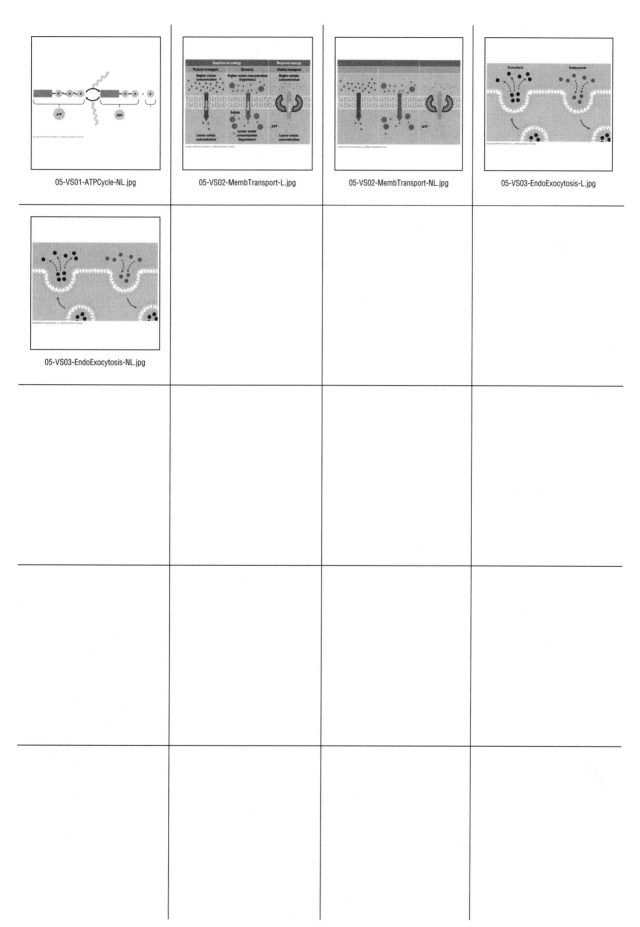

05-VS01-ATPCycle-NL.jpg

05-VS02-MembTransport-L.jpg

05-VS02-MembTransport-NL.jpg

05-VS03-EndoExocytosis-L.jpg

05-VS03-EndoExocytosis-NL.jpg

Chapter 6 Cellular Respiration: Harvesting Chemical Energy

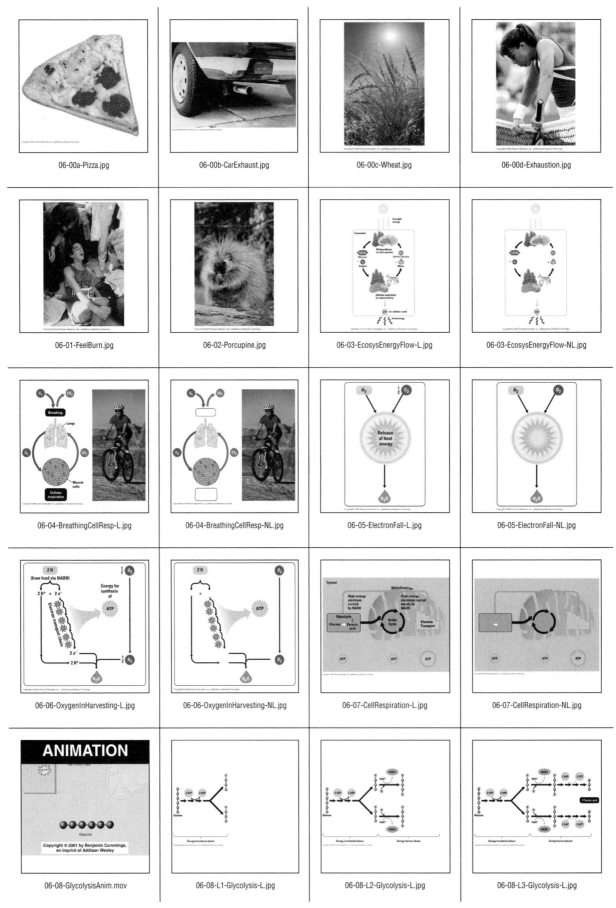

06-00a-Pizza.jpg

06-00b-CarExhaust.jpg

06-00c-Wheat.jpg

06-00d-Exhaustion.jpg

06-01-FeelBurn.jpg

06-02-Porcupine.jpg

06-03-EcosysEnergyFlow-L.jpg

06-03-EcosysEnergyFlow-NL.jpg

06-04-BreathingCellResp-L.jpg

06-04-BreathingCellResp-NL.jpg

06-05-ElectronFall-L.jpg

06-05-ElectronFall-NL.jpg

06-06-OxygenInHarvesting-L.jpg

06-06-OxygenInHarvesting-NL.jpg

06-07-CellRespiration-L.jpg

06-07-CellRespiration-NL.jpg

06-08-GlycolysisAnim.mov

06-08-L1-Glycolysis-L.jpg

06-08-L2-Glycolysis-L.jpg

06-08-L3-Glycolysis-L.jpg

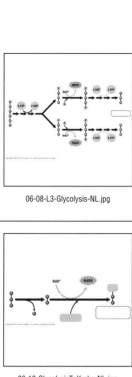

06-08-L3-Glycolysis-NL.jpg

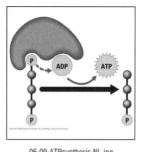

06-09-ATPsynthesis-L.jpg

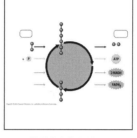

06-09-ATPsynthesis-NL.jpg

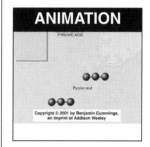

06-10-GlycolysisToKrebs-L.jpg

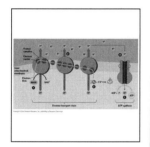

06-10-GlycolysisToKrebs-NL.jpg

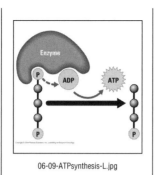

06-11-KrebsCycle-L.jpg

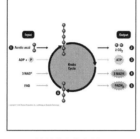

06-11-KrebsCycle-NL.jpg

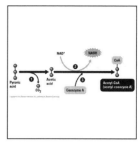

06-11-KrebsCycleAnim.mov

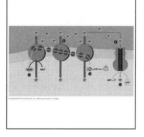

06-12-ElectronTransport-L.jpg

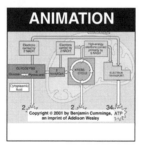

06-12-ElectronTransport-NL.jpg

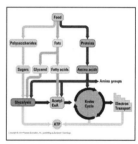

06-12-ElectronTransportAnim.mov

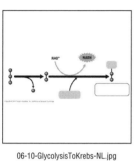

06-13-EnergyFromFood-L.jpg

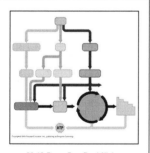

06-13-EnergyFromFood-NL.jpg

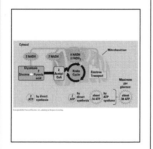

06-14-CellRespiration-L.jpg

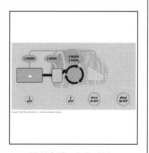

06-14-CellRespiration-NL.jpg

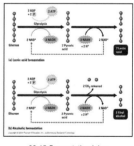

06-15-Fermentation-L.jpg

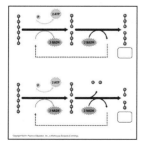

06-15-Fermentation-NL.jpg

06-16-Fermentation.jpg

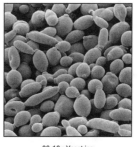

06-16x-Yeast.jpg

06-UN-Oxidation-L.jpg

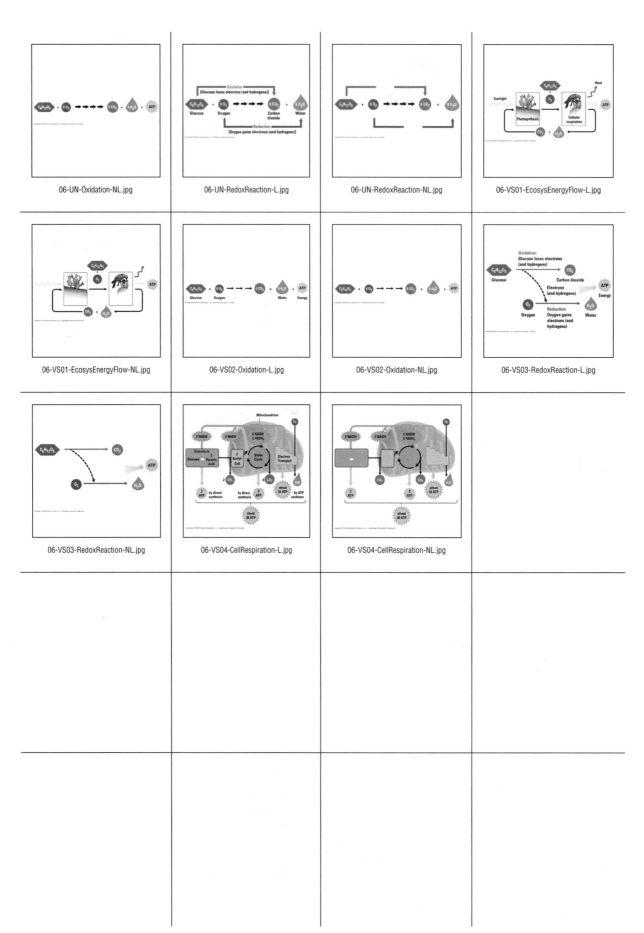

06-UN-Oxidation-NL.jpg

06-UN-RedoxReaction-L.jpg

06-UN-RedoxReaction-NL.jpg

06-VS01-EcosysEnergyFlow-L.jpg

06-VS01-EcosysEnergyFlow-NL.jpg

06-VS02-Oxidation-L.jpg

06-VS02-Oxidation-NL.jpg

06-VS03-RedoxReaction-L.jpg

06-VS03-RedoxReaction-NL.jpg

06-VS04-CellRespiration-L.jpg

06-VS04-CellRespiration-NL.jpg

Chapter 7 Photosynthesis: Converting Light Energy to Chemical Energy

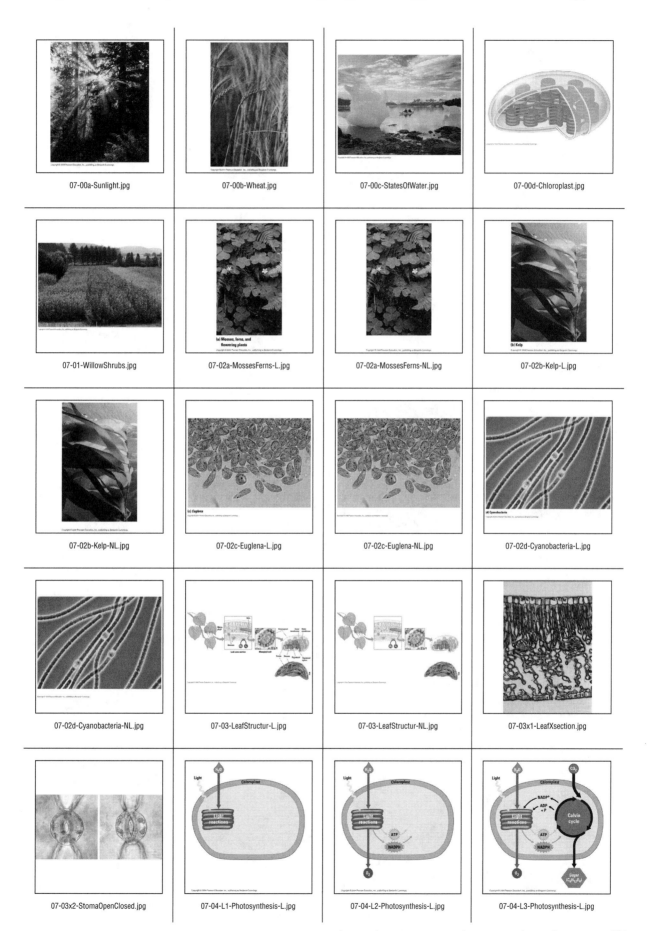

07-00a-Sunlight.jpg

07-00b-Wheat.jpg

07-00c-StatesOfWater.jpg

07-00d-Chloroplast.jpg

07-01-WillowShrubs.jpg

07-02a-MossesFerns-L.jpg

07-02a-MossesFerns-NL.jpg

07-02b-Kelp-L.jpg

07-02b-Kelp-NL.jpg

07-02c-Euglena-L.jpg

07-02c-Euglena-NL.jpg

07-02d-Cyanobacteria-L.jpg

07-02d-Cyanobacteria-NL.jpg

07-03-LeafStructur-L.jpg

07-03-LeafStructur-NL.jpg

07-03x1-LeafXsection.jpg

07-03x2-StomaOpenClosed.jpg

07-04-L1-Photosynthesis-L.jpg

07-04-L2-Photosynthesis-L.jpg

07-04-L3-Photosynthesis-L.jpg

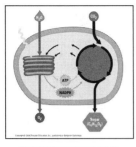
07-04-L3-Photosynthesis-NL.jpg

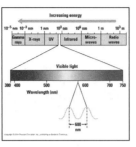
07-05-ElectromagSpectrum-L.jpg

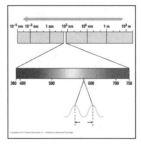
07-05-ElectromagSpectrum-NL.jpg

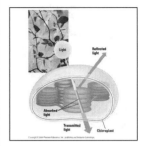
07-06-ReflectionOfGreen-L.jpg

07-06-ReflectionOfGreen-NL.jpg

07-06x-ChlorophyllModel.jpg

07-07-FallFoliage.jpg

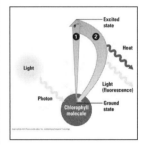
07-08a-Photon-L.jpg

07-08a-Photon-NL.jpg

07-08b-Fluorescence.jpg

07-08c-GlowStick.jpg

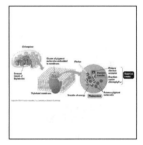
07-09-Photosystem-L.jpg

07-09-Photosystem-NL.jpg

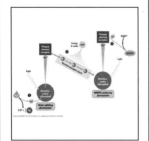
07-10-LightReactions-L.jpg

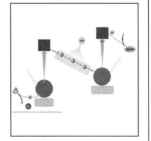
07-10-LightReactions-NL.jpg

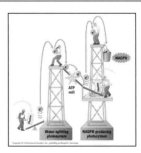
07-11-LightReactions-L.jpg

07-11-LightReactions-NL.jpg

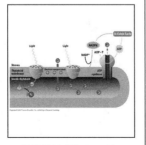
07-12-ThylakoidMembrane-L.jpg

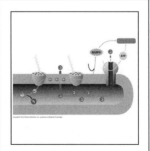
07-12-ThylakoidMembrane-NL.jpg

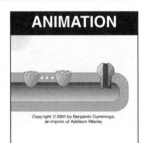
07-12-ThylaMembraneAnim.mov

07-13-CalvinCycleAnim.mov

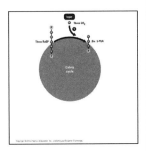

07-13-L1-CalvinCycle-L.jpg

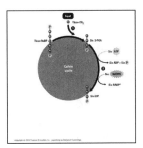

07-13-L2-CalvinCycle-L.jpg

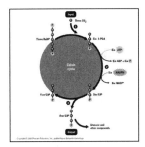

07-13-L3-CalvinCycle-L.jpg

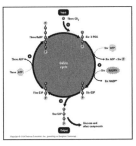

07-13-L4-CalvinCycle-L.jpg

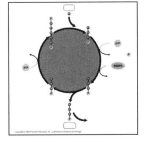

07-13-L4-CalvinCycle-NL.jpg

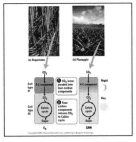

07-14-C4CAM-L.jpg

07-14-C4CAM-NL.jpg

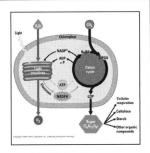

07-15-Photosynthesis-L.jpg

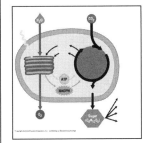

07-15-Photosynthesis-NL.jpg

07-16-OldGrowthForest.jpg

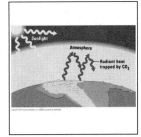

07-17-GreenhouseEffect-L.jpg

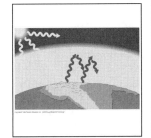

07-17-GreenhouseEffect-NL.jpg

07-UNp.105-Photosynthesi-NL.jpg

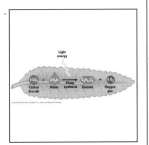

07-UNp.105-Photosynthesis-L.jpg

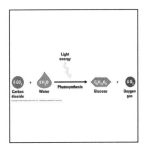

07-VS01-Photosynthesis-L.jpg

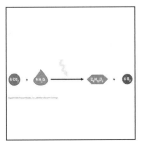

07-VS01-Photosynthesis-NL.jpg

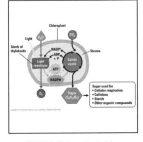

07-VS02-Photosynthesis-L.jpg

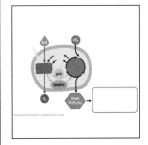

07-VS02-Photosynthesis-NL.jpg

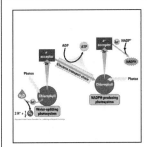

07-VS03-LightReactions-L.jpg

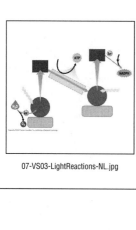

07-VS03-LightReactions-NL.jpg

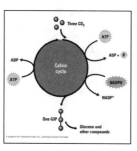

07-VS04-CalvinCycle-L.jpg

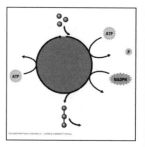

07-VS04-CalvinCycle-NL.jpg

Chapter 8 The Cellular Basis of Reproduction and Inheritance

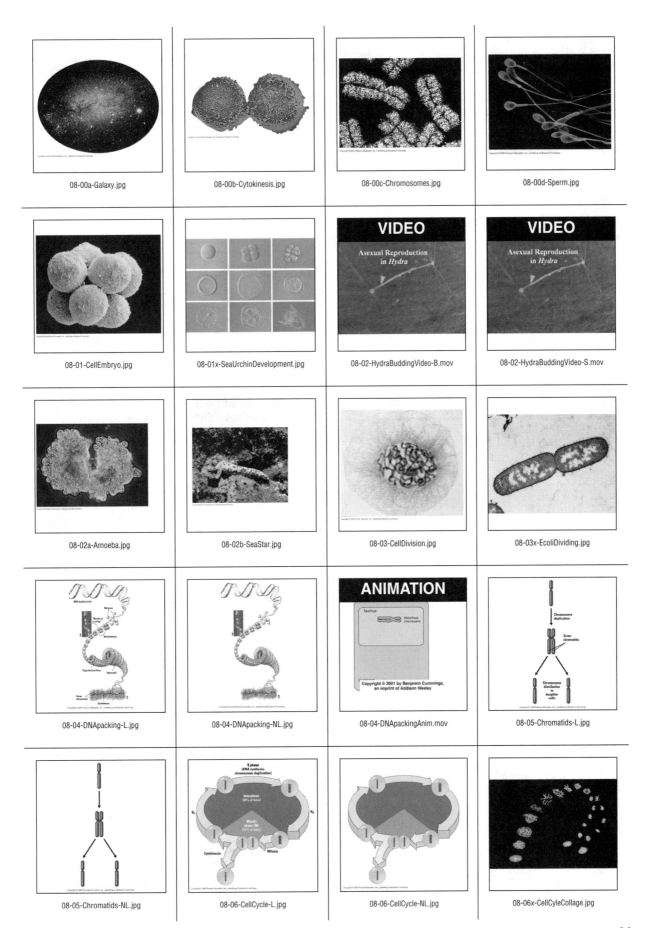

08-00a-Galaxy.jpg

08-00b-Cytokinesis.jpg

08-00c-Chromosomes.jpg

08-00d-Sperm.jpg

08-01-CellEmbryo.jpg

08-01x-SeaUrchinDevelopment.jpg

08-02-HydraBuddingVideo-B.mov

08-02-HydraBuddingVideo-S.mov

08-02a-Amoeba.jpg

08-02b-SeaStar.jpg

08-03-CellDivision.jpg

08-03x-EcoliDividing.jpg

08-04-DNApacking-L.jpg

08-04-DNApacking-NL.jpg

08-04-DNApackingAnim.mov

08-05-Chromatids-L.jpg

08-05-Chromatids-NL.jpg

08-06-CellCycle-L.jpg

08-06-CellCycle-NL.jpg

08-06x-CellCyleCollage.jpg

08-07-AnimalMitosisVideo-B.mov

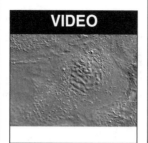

08-07-AnimalMitosisVideo-S.mov

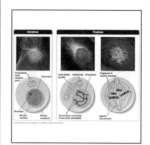

08-07a-InterphasProphas-L.jpg

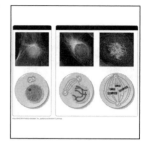

08-07a-InterphasProphas-NL.jpg

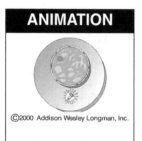

08-07a-MitosisOverviewAnim.mov

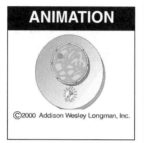

08-07b-LateInterphaseAnim.mov

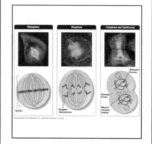

08-07b-MetaAnaTeloCyto-L.jpg

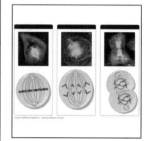

08-07b-MetaAnaTeloCyto-NL.jpg

08-07c-ProphaseAnim.mov

08-07d-LateProphaseAnim.mov

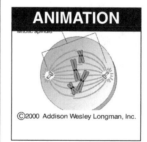

08-07e-MetaphaseAnim.mov

08-07f-AnaphaseAnim.mov

08-07g-TelophaseAnim.mov

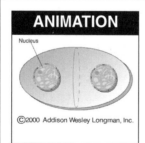

08-07h-CytokinesisAnim.mov

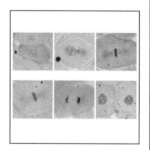

08-07x1-MitosisCollage.jpg

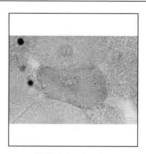

08-07x1a-Interphase.jpg

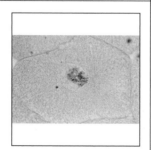

08-07x1b-EarlyProphase.jpg

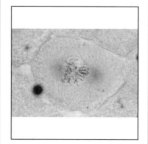

08-07x1c-LateProphase.jpg

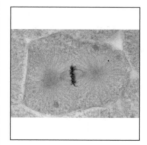

08-07x1d-Metaphase.jpg

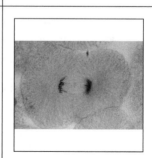

08-07x1e-Anaphase.jpg

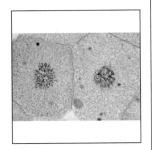

08-07x1f-LateTelophase.jpg

08-07x2-MitoticSpindle.jpg

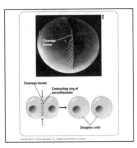

08-08a-AnimalCytokinesis-L.jpg

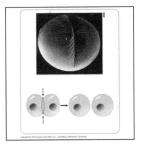

08-08a-AnimalCytokinesis-NL.jpg

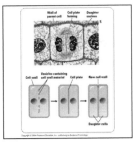

08-08b-PlantCytokinesis-L.jpg

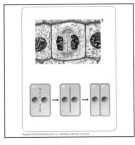

08-08b-PlantCytokinesis-NL.jpg

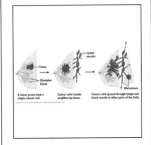

08-09-CancerMetastasis-L.jpg

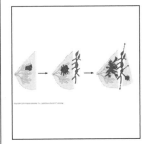

08-09-CancerMetastasis-NL.jpg

08-09x-FibroblastGrowth.jpg

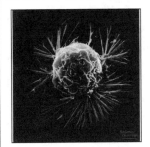

08-09x1-BreastCancerCell.jpg

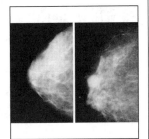

08-09x2-MammogramsNrmlCancr.jpg

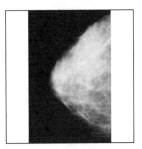

08-09x2a-MammogramNormal.jpg

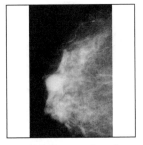

08-09x2b-MammogramCancer.jpg

08-10-LabCancerCells.jpg

08-11-SexVariation.jpg

08-12-NormalKaryotype-L.jpg

08-12-NormalKaryotype-NL.jpg

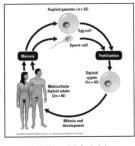

08-13-HumanLifeCycle-L.jpg

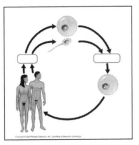

08-13-HumanLifeCycle-NL.jpg

08-14-Meiosis-L.jpg

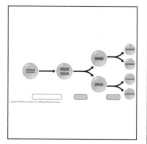

08-14-Meiosis-NL.jpg

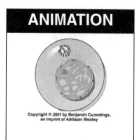

08-15a-InterphaseIAnim.mov

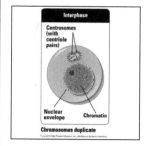

08-15a-MeiosisInterphas-L.jpg

08-15a-MeiosisInterphas-NL.jpg

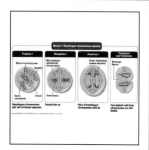

08-15b-MeiosisI-L.jpg

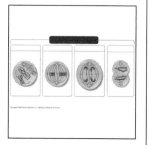

08-15b-MeiosisI-NL.jpg

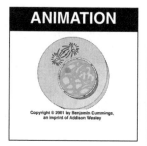

08-15b-ProphaseIAnim.mov

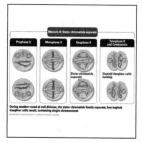

08-15c-MeiosisII-L.jpg

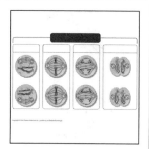

08-15c-MeiosisII-NL.jpg

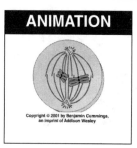

08-15c-MetaphaseIAnim.mov

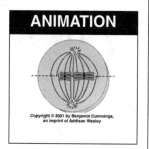

08-15d-AnaphaseIAnim.mov

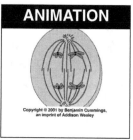

08-15e-TelophaseICytokAnim.mov

08-15f-MeiosisIICytokAnim.mov

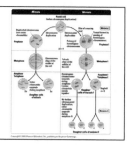

08-16-MitosisMeiosis-L.jpg

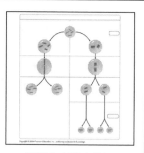

08-16-MitosisMeiosis-NL.jpg

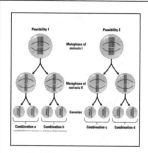

08-17-MetaphasVariation-L.jpg

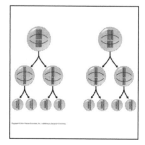

08-17-MetaphasVariation-NL.jpg

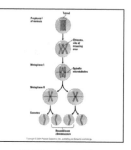

08-18-CrossingOver-L.jpg

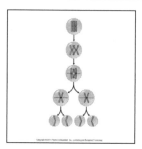

08-18-CrossingOver-NL.jpg

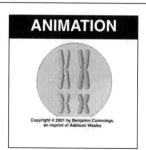

08-18-CrossingOverAnim.mov

08-19-Trisomy21Karyotype.jpg

08-19x1-HumanFemaleChromosm.jpg

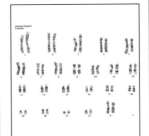

08-19x2-HumanFemaleKaryotyp.jpg

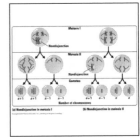

08-19x3-HumanMaleChromosoms.jpg

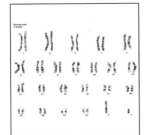

08-19x4-HumanMaleKaryotype.jpg

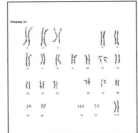

08-19x5-DownKaryotypeBW.jpg

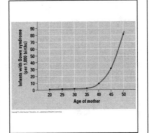

08-20-DownMaternalAge-L.jpg

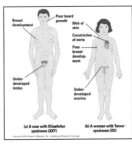

08-21-Nondisjunction-L.jpg

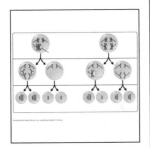

08-21-Nondisjunction-NL.jpg

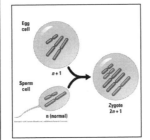

08-22-AneuploidyTrisomy-L.jpg

08-22-AneuploidyTrisomy-NL.jpg

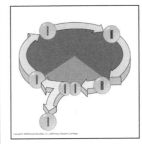

08-23-XXYXO-L.jpg

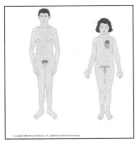

08-23-XXYXO-NL.jpg

08-23ax-KlinefelterKaryotyp.jpg

08-23bx-TranslocationPhoto.gif

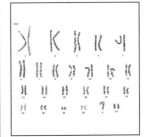

08-23x-XYYkaryotype.jpg

08-24-TetraploidRat.jpg

08-T01-ChromAbnornalities.jpg

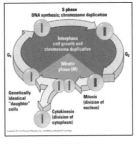

08-VS01-CellCycle-L.jpg

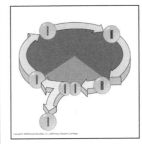

08-VS01-CellCycle-NL.jpg

Chapter 9 Patterns of Inheritance

09-00a-Mendel.jpg

09-00b-FlyMalaria.jpg

09-00c-NormalKaryotype.jpg

09-00d-QueenVictoria.jpg

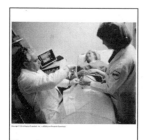

09-01-Amniocentesis.jpg

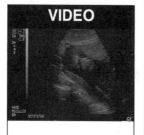

09-01-Ultrasound1Video-B.mov

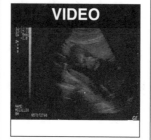

09-01-Ultrasound1Video-S.mov

09-01-Ultrasound2Video-S.mov

09-02-BudgieVariation.jpg

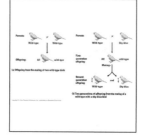

09-03-BudgieInheritance-L.jpg

09-03-BudgieInheritance-NL.jpg

09-04-Mendel.jpg

09-04x-GregorMendel.jpg

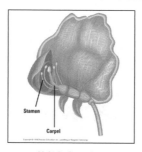

09-05-PeaFlower-L.jpg

09-05-PeaFlower-NL.jpg

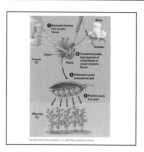

09-06-MendelsPeas-L.jpg

09-06-MendelsPeas-NL.jpg

09-07-MendelsPeas-L.jpg

09-07-MendelsPeas-NL.jpg

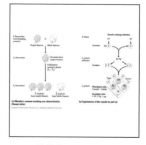

09-08-Segregation-L.jpg

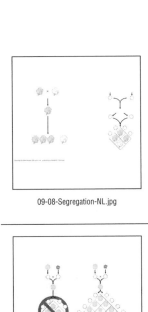

09-08-Segregation-NL.jpg

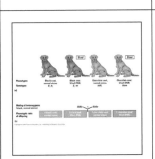

09-09-HomologousPair-L.jpg

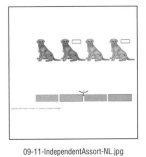

09-09-HomologousPair-NL.jpg

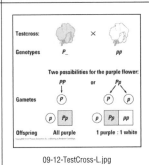

09-10-GeneAssortment-L.jpg

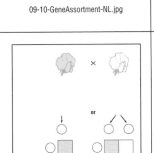

09-10-GeneAssortment-NL.jpg

09-11-IndependentAssort-L.jpg

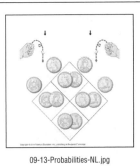

09-11-IndependentAssort-NL.jpg

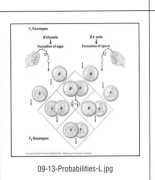

09-12-TestCross-L.jpg

09-12-TestCross-NL.jpg

09-12x-PurpleWhiteFlowers.jpg

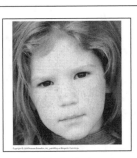

09-13-Probabilities-L.jpg

09-13-Probabilities-NL.jpg

09-14-InheritedTraits-L.jpg

09-14-InheritedTraits-NL.jpg

09-14a-Freckles.jpg

09-14b-NoFreckles.jpg

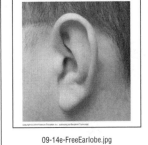

09-14c-WidowsPeak.jpg

09-14d-NoWidowsPeak.jpg

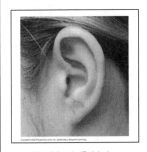

09-14e-FreeEarlobe.jpg

09-14f-AttachedEarlobe.jpg

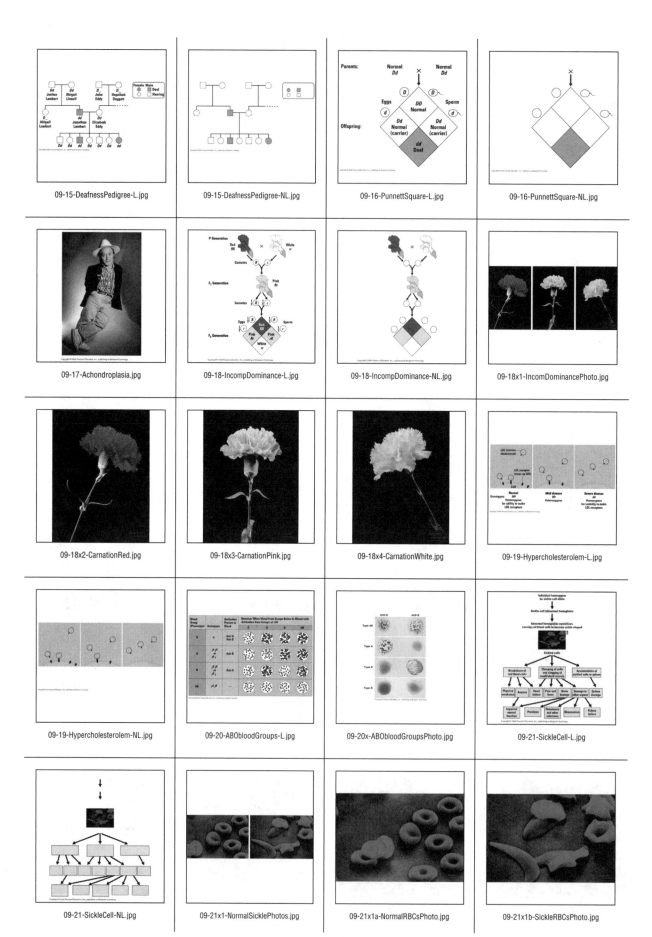

09-15-DeafnessPedigree-L.jpg

09-15-DeafnessPedigree-NL.jpg

09-16-PunnettSquare-L.jpg

09-16-PunnettSquare-NL.jpg

09-17-Achondroplasia.jpg

09-18-IncompDominance-L.jpg

09-18-IncompDominance-NL.jpg

09-18x1-IncomDominancePhoto.jpg

09-18x2-CarnationRed.jpg

09-18x3-CarnationPink.jpg

09-18x4-CarnationWhite.jpg

09-19-Hypercholesterolem-L.jpg

09-19-Hypercholesterolem-NL.jpg

09-20-ABObloodGroups-L.jpg

09-20x-ABObloodGroupsPhoto.jpg

09-21-SickleCell-L.jpg

09-21-SickleCell-NL.jpg

09-21x1-NormalSicklePhotos.jpg

09-21x1a-NormalRBCsPhoto.jpg

09-21x1b-SickleRBCsPhoto.jpg

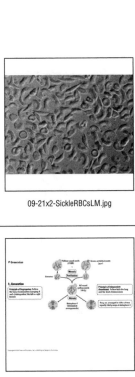

09-21x2-SickleRBCsLM.jpg

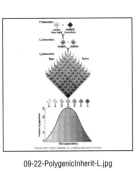

09-22-PolygenicInherit-L.jpg

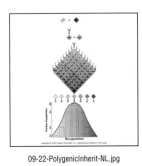

09-22-PolygenicInherit-NL.jpg

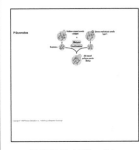

09-23-L1-DihybridCross-L.jpg

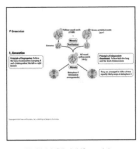

09-23-L2-DihybridCross-L.jpg

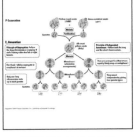

09-23-L3-DihybridCross-L.jpg

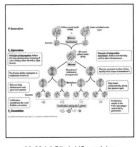

09-23-L4-DihybridCross-L.jpg

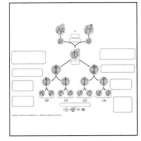

09-23-L4-DihybridCross-NL.jpg

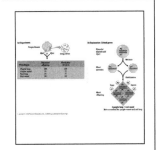

09-24ab-LinkedGenesCross-L.jpg

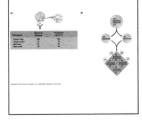

09-24ab-LinkedGenesCross-NL.jpg

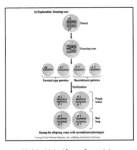

09-24c-LinkedGenesCross-L.jpg

09-24c-LinkedGenesCross-NL.jpg

09-25-FruitFlyVariants-L.jpg

09-25-FruitFlyVariants-NL.jpg

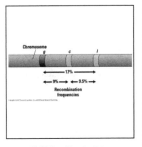

09-26-GeneMapping-L.jpg

09-26-GeneMapping-NL.jpg

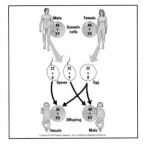

09-27-SexDetermination-L.jpg

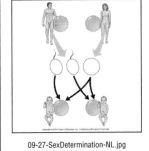

09-27-SexDetermination-NL.jpg

09-28-FruitFlyEyeColor.jpg

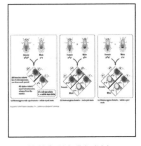

09-29-SexLinkedInherit-L.jpg

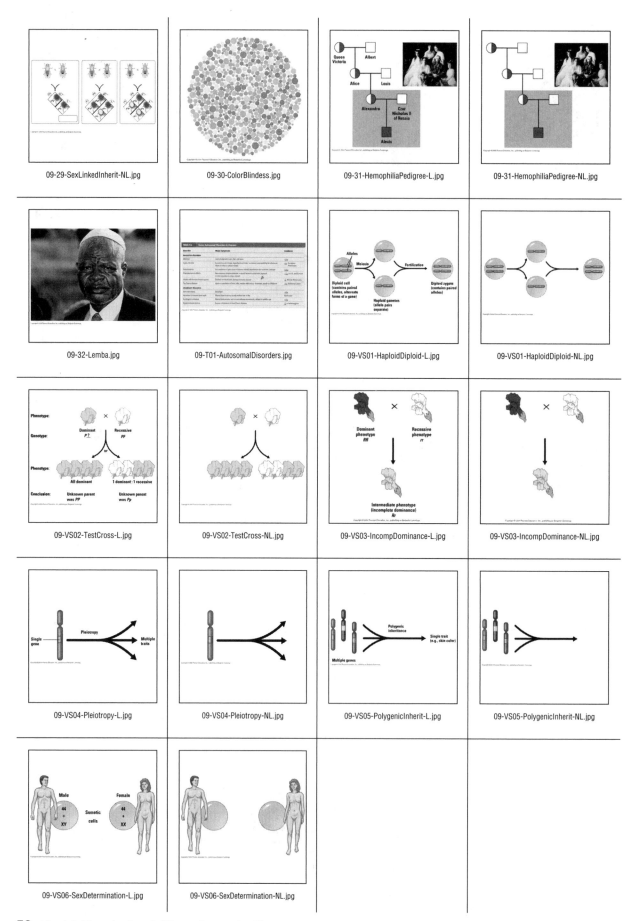

09-29-SexLinkedInherit-NL.jpg

09-30-ColorBlindess.jpg

09-31-HemophiliaPedigree-L.jpg

09-31-HemophiliaPedigree-NL.jpg

09-32-Lemba.jpg

09-T01-AutosomalDisorders.jpg

09-VS01-HaploidDiploid-L.jpg

09-VS01-HaploidDiploid-NL.jpg

09-VS02-TestCross-L.jpg

09-VS02-TestCross-NL.jpg

09-VS03-IncompDominance-L.jpg

09-VS03-IncompDominance-NL.jpg

09-VS04-Pleiotropy-L.jpg

09-VS04-Pleiotropy-NL.jpg

09-VS05-PolygenicInherit-L.jpg

09-VS05-PolygenicInherit-NL.jpg

09-VS06-SexDetermination-L.jpg

09-VS06-SexDetermination-NL.jpg

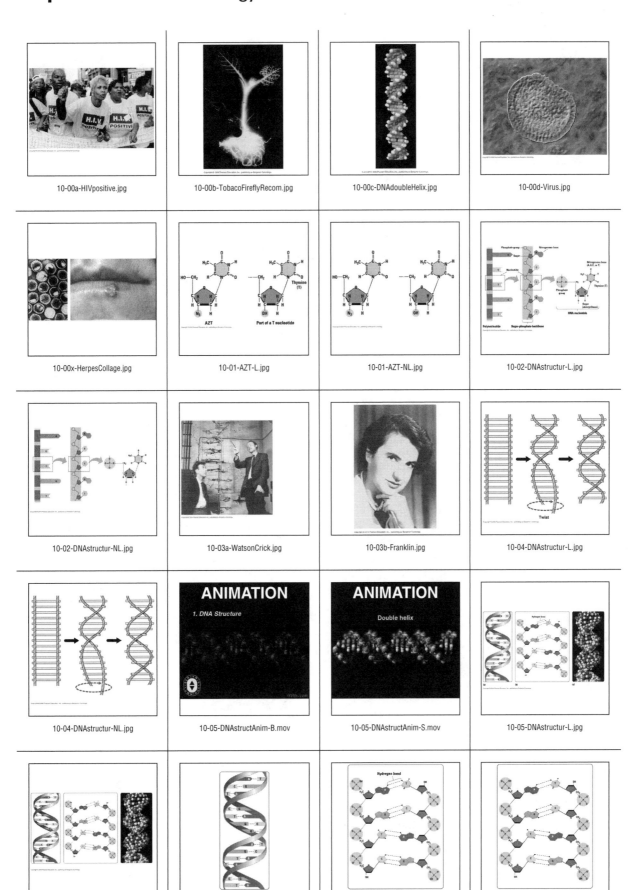

10-00a-HIVpositive.jpg

10-00b-TobacoFireflyRecom.jpg

10-00c-DNAdoubleHelix.jpg

10-00d-Virus.jpg

10-00x-HerpesCollage.jpg

10-01-AZT-L.jpg

10-01-AZT-NL.jpg

10-02-DNAstructur-L.jpg

10-02-DNAstructur-NL.jpg

10-03a-WatsonCrick.jpg

10-03b-Franklin.jpg

10-04-DNAstructur-L.jpg

10-04-DNAstructur-NL.jpg

10-05-DNAstructAnim-B.mov

10-05-DNAstructAnim-S.mov

10-05-DNAstructur-L.jpg

10-05-DNAstructur-NL.jpg

10-05a-BlueRibbonDNA.jpg

10-05b-CompDNA-L.jpg

10-05b-CompDNA-NL.jpg

10-05c-ChemStrucDNA.jpg

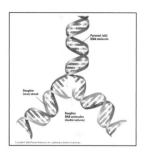

10-06-DNAreplication-L.jpg

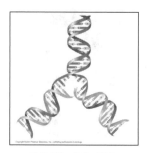

10-06-DNAreplication-NL.jpg

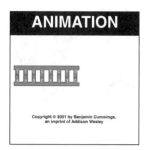

10-06-DNArepOverviewAnim.mov

10-07-UVdamage.jpg

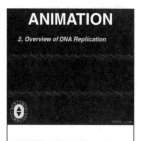

10-08-DNArepliAnim-B.mov

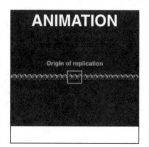

10-08-DNArepliAnim-S.mov

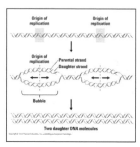

10-08-ReplicationBubbles-L.jpg

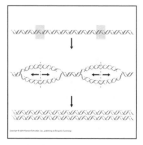

10-08-ReplicationBubbles-NL.jpg

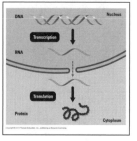

10-09-GeneticInfoFlow-L.jpg

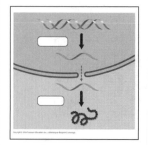

10-09-GeneticInfoFlow-NL.jpg

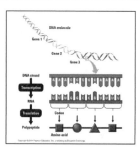

10-10-TranscripTranslat-L.jpg

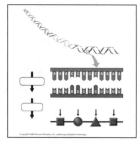

10-10-TranscripTranslat-NL.jpg

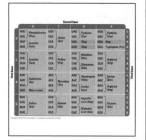

10-11-GeneticCode.jpg

10-12-TobacoFireflyRecom.jpg

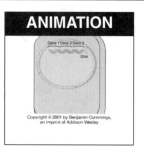

10-13-TranscriptionAnim.mov

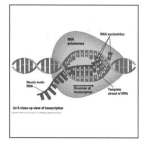

10-13a-Transcription-L.jpg

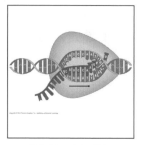

10-13a-Transcription-NL.jpg

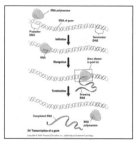

10-13b-TranscriptionGene-L.jpg

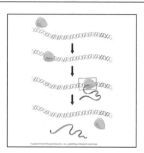

10-13b-TranscriptionGene-NL.jpg

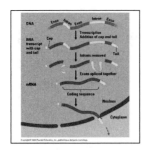

10-14-mRNAproduction-L.jpg

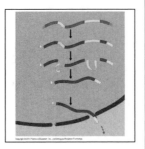

10-14-mRNAproduction-NL.jpg

10-14-RNAprocessingAnim.mov

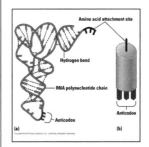

10-15-tRNAstructur-L.jpg

10-15-tRNAstructur-NL.jpg

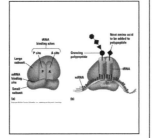

10-16-RibosomeStructur-L.jpg

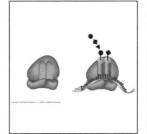

10-16-RibosomeStructur-NL.jpg

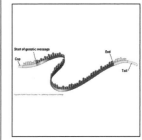

10-17-mRNA-L.jpg

10-17-mRNA-NL.jpg

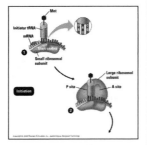

10-18-Initiation-L.jpg

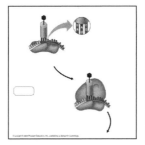

10-18-Initiation-NL.jpg

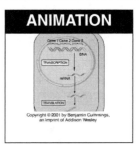

10-18-TranslationAnim.mov

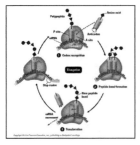

10-19-Elongation-L.jpg

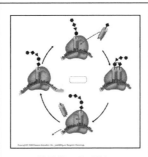

10-19-Elongation-NL.jpg

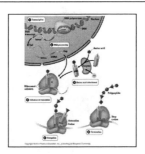

10-20-TranscripTranslat-L.jpg

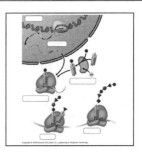

10-20-TranscripTranslat-NL.jpg

10-21-SickleCellMutation-L.jpg

10-21-SickleCellMutation-NL.jpg

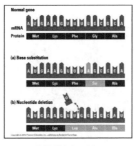

10-22-Mutations-L.jpg

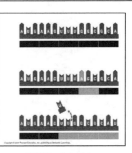

10-22-Mutations-NL.jpg

10-23-MutationDiversity.jpg

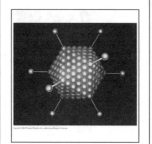

10-24-Adenovirus.jpg

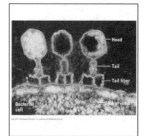

10-25-PhageInfectsCell-L.jpg

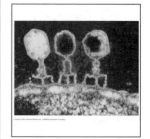

10-25-PhageInfectsCell-NL.jpg

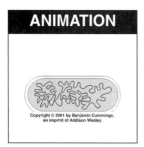

10-25-PhageT2ReproAnim.mov

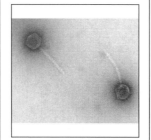

10-25x-Phages.jpg

10-26-L1-PhageReproCyc-L.jpg

10-26-L2-PhageReproCyc-L.jpg

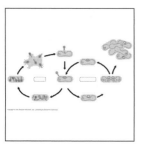

10-26-L2-PhageReproCyc-NL.jpg

10-26-PhageReproAnim.mov

10-27-TobaccoMosaicVirus-L.jpg

10-27-TobaccoMosaicVirus-NL.jpg

10-27x-TobaccoVirusPhoto.jpg

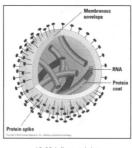

10-28-Influenza-L.jpg

10-28-Influenza-NL.jpg

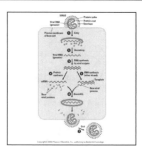

10-29-EnvelopedVirus-L.jpg

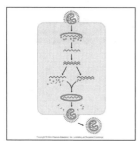

10-29-EnvelopedVirus-NL.jpg

10-29x-PolioVictim.jpg

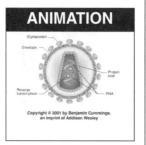

10-30-HIVreproductionAnim.mov

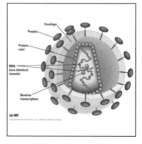

10-30a-HIVinfection-L.jpg

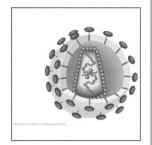

10-30a-HIVinfection-NL.jpg

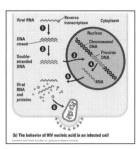

10-30b-HIVinfection-L.jpg

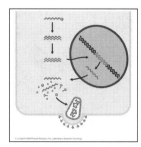

10-30b-HIVinfection-NL.jpg

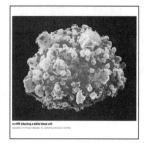

10-30c-HIVinfection.jpg

10-30x1-HIVinfectionTEM.jpg

10-30x2-AIDSquilt.jpg

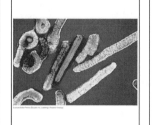

10-31a-Ebola.jpg

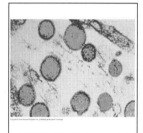

10-31b-Hantavirus.jpg

10-31x-DeerMouse.jpg

10-32-SARSvirus.jpg

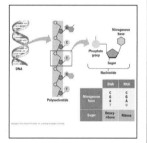

10-VS01-DNAstructur-L.jpg

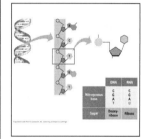

10-VS01-DNAstructur-NL.jpg

10-VS02-DNAreplication-L.jpg

10-VS02-DNAreplication-NL.jpg

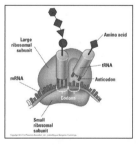

10-VS03-Translation-L.jpg

10-VS03-Translation-NL.jpg

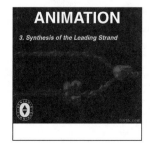

10x1-LeadingStrandAnim-B.mov

10x1-LeadingStrandAnim-S.mov

10x2-LaggingStrandAnim-B.mov

10x2-LaggingStrandAnim-S.mov

10x3-LaggingStrandAnim-B.mov

10x3-LaggingStrandAnim-S.mov

Chapter 11 Gene Regulation

11-00a-Human.jpg

11-00b-Salamander.jpg

11-00c-Chicken.jpg

11-00d-SmokingCancer.jpg

11-01a-UmbilicalCord.jpg

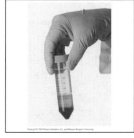

11-01b-UmbBlood.jpg

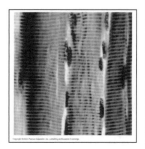

11-02a-MuscleCells.jpg

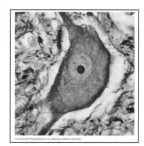

11-02b-NerveCell.jpg

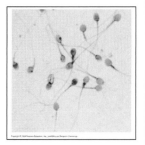

11-02c-SpermCells.jpg

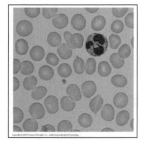

11-02d-BloodCells.jpg

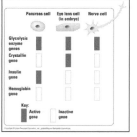

11-03-GeneExp-L.jpg

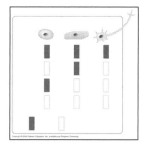

11-03-GeneExp-NL.jpg

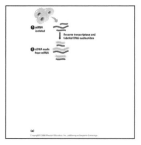

11-04a-L1-cDNAL.jpg

11-04a-L2-cDNAMic-L.jpg

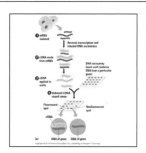

11-04a-L3-Microar-L.jpg

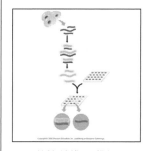

11-04a-L3-Microar-NL.jpg

11-04A-ScieWkVideo-B.mov

11-04b-Microarray-L.jpg

11-04b-Microarray-NL.jpg

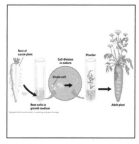

11-05-CarrotClone-L.jpg

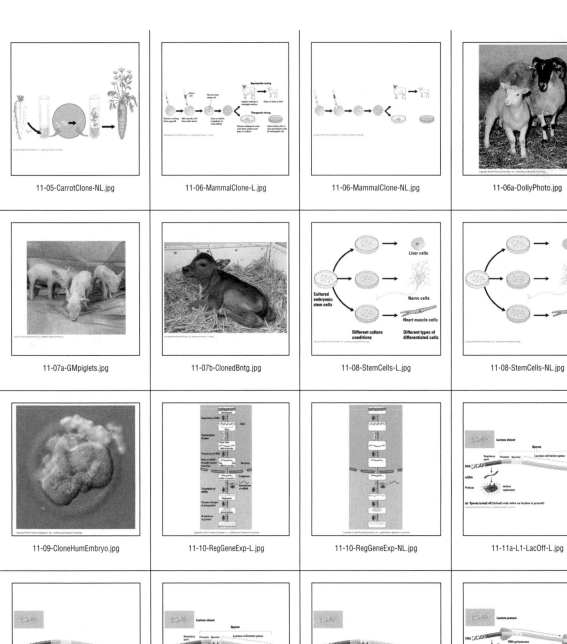

11-05-CarrotClone-NL.jpg

11-06-MammalClone-L.jpg

11-06-MammalClone-NL.jpg

11-06a-DollyPhoto.jpg

11-07a-GMpiglets.jpg

11-07b-ClonedBntg.jpg

11-08-StemCells-L.jpg

11-08-StemCells-NL.jpg

11-09-CloneHumEmbryo.jpg

11-10-RegGeneExp-L.jpg

11-10-RegGeneExp-NL.jpg

11-11a-L1-LacOff-L.jpg

11-11a-L1-LacOff-NL.jpg

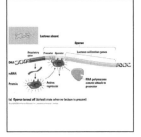

11-11a-L2-LacOff-L.jpg

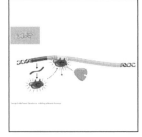

11-11a-L2-LacOff-NL.jpg

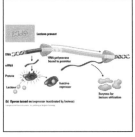

11-11b-LacOperOn-L.jpg

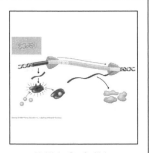

11-11b-LacOperOn-NL.jpg

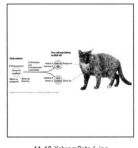

11-12-XchromCats-L.jpg

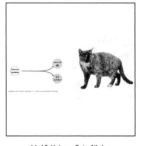

11-12-XchromCats-NL.jpg

11-12x-CalicoCat.jpg

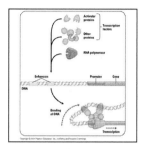

11-13-EukGeneReg-L.jpg

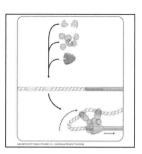

11-13-EukGeneReg-NL.jpg

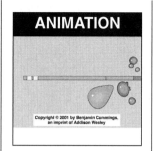

11-13-TrngOnGeneAnim.mov

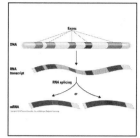

11-14-SpliceRNA-L.jpg

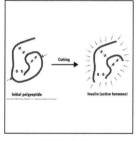

11-14-SpliceRNA-NL.jpg

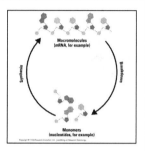

11-15-RecyclMolec-L.jpg

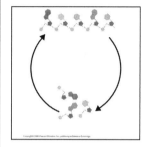

11-15-RecyclMolec-NL.jpg

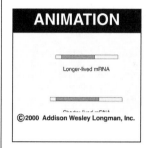

11-16-CntrlTransAnim.mov

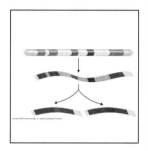

11-16-Insulin-L.jpg

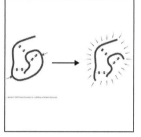

11-16-Insulin-NL.jpg

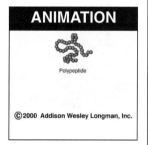

11-16-ProtProdAnim.mov

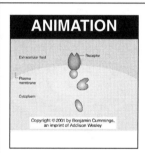

11-17-CellSignlAnim.mov

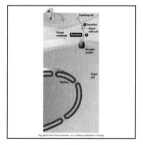

11-17-L1-CellSignal.jpg

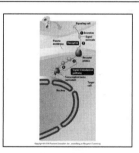

11-17-L2-SigTransduc.jpg

11-17-L3-SigTransduc.jpg

11-17-L4-CellSig-L.jpg

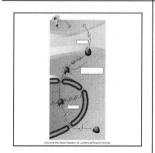

11-17-L4-CellSig-NL.jpg

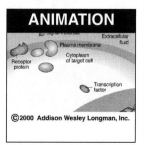

11-17-SignlTrnsdAnim.mov

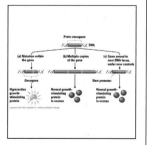

11-18-Oncogenes-L.jpg

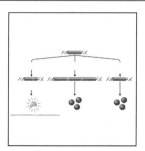

11-18-Oncogenes-NL.jpg

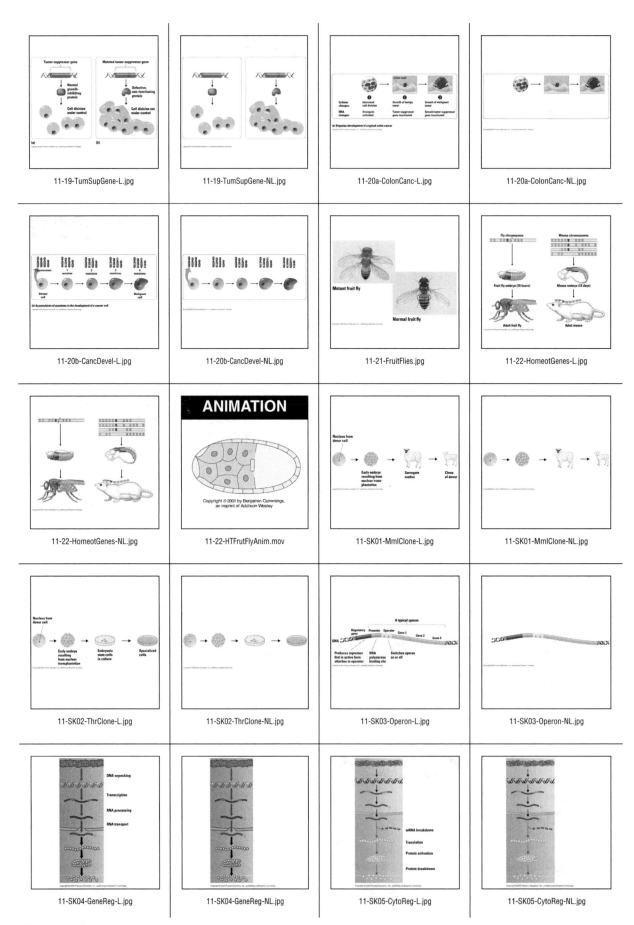

11-19-TumSupGene-L.jpg

11-19-TumSupGene-NL.jpg

11-20a-ColonCanc-L.jpg

11-20a-ColonCanc-NL.jpg

11-20b-CancDevel-L.jpg

11-20b-CancDevel-NL.jpg

11-21-FruitFlies.jpg

11-22-HomeotGenes-L.jpg

11-22-HomeotGenes-NL.jpg

11-22-HTFrutFlyAnim.mov

11-SK01-MmlClone-L.jpg

11-SK01-MmlClone-NL.jpg

11-SK02-ThrClone-L.jpg

11-SK02-ThrClone-NL.jpg

11-SK03-Operon-L.jpg

11-SK03-Operon-NL.jpg

11-SK04-GeneReg-L.jpg

11-SK04-GeneReg-NL.jpg

11-SK05-CytoReg-L.jpg

11-SK05-CytoReg-NL.jpg

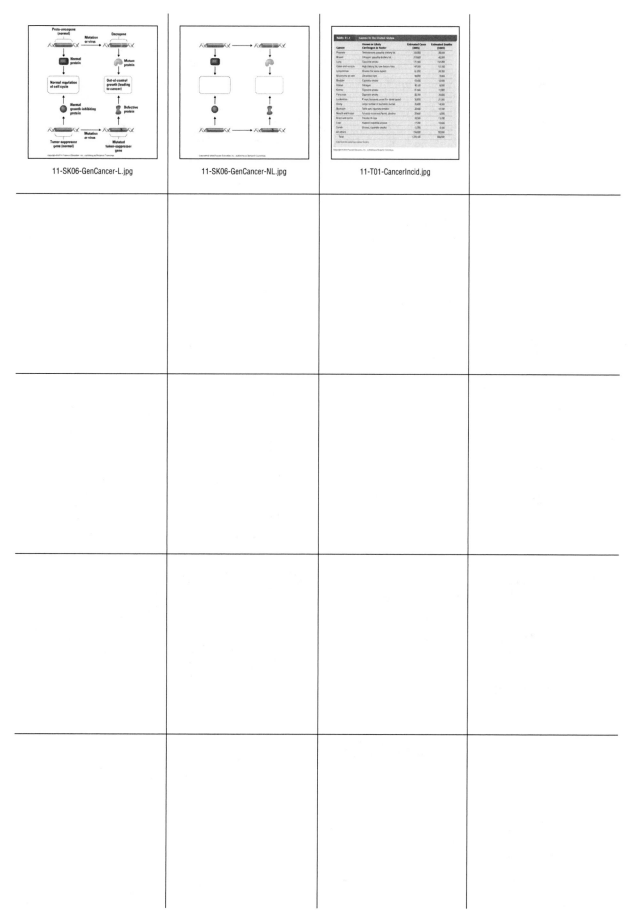

11-SK06-GenCancer-L.jpg

11-SK06-GenCancer-NL.jpg

11-T01-CancerIncid.jpg

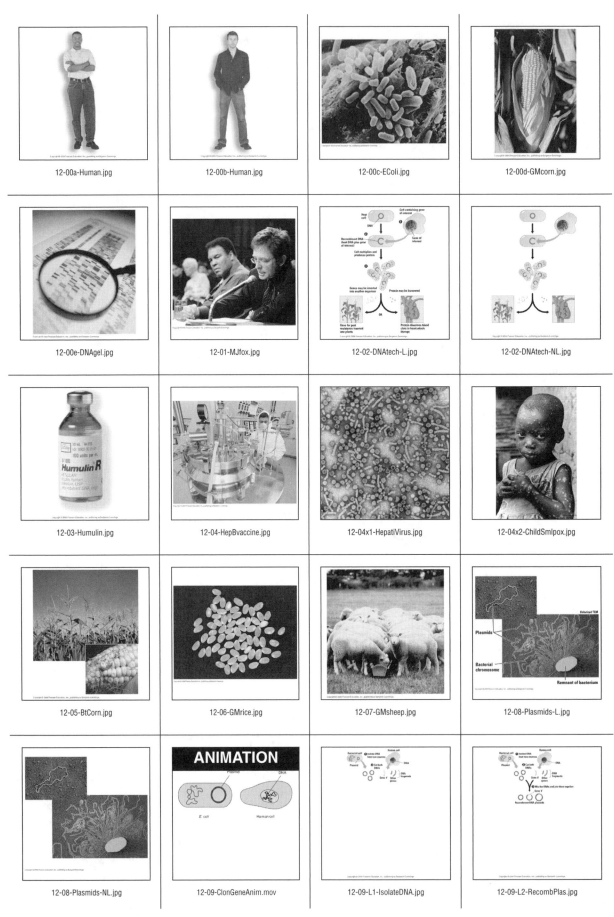

12-00a-Human.jpg

12-00b-Human.jpg

12-00c-EColi.jpg

12-00d-GMcorn.jpg

12-00e-DNAgel.jpg

12-01-MJfox.jpg

12-02-DNAtech-L.jpg

12-02-DNAtech-NL.jpg

12-03-Humulin.jpg

12-04-HepBvaccine.jpg

12-04x1-HepatiVirus.jpg

12-04x2-ChildSmlpox.jpg

12-05-BtCorn.jpg

12-06-GMrice.jpg

12-07-GMsheep.jpg

12-08-Plasmids-L.jpg

12-08-Plasmids-NL.jpg

12-09-ClonGeneAnim.mov

12-09-L1-IsolateDNA.jpg

12-09-L2-RecombPlas.jpg

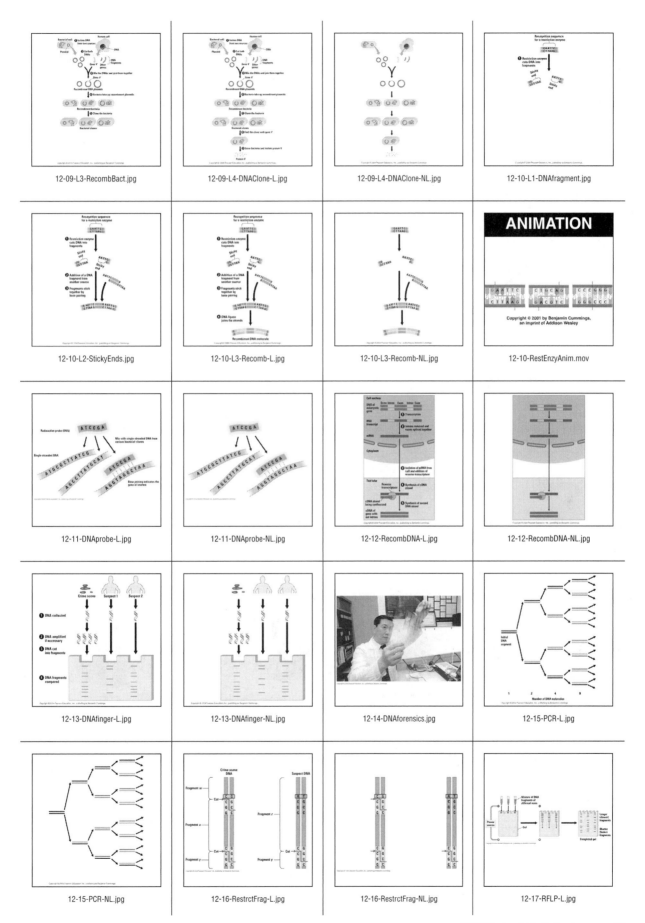

12-09-L3-RecombBact.jpg

12-09-L4-DNAClone-L.jpg

12-09-L4-DNAClone-NL.jpg

12-10-L1-DNAfragment.jpg

12-10-L2-StickyEnds.jpg

12-10-L3-Recomb-L.jpg

12-10-L3-Recomb-NL.jpg

12-10-RestEnzyAnim.mov

12-11-DNAprobe-L.jpg

12-11-DNAprobe-NL.jpg

12-12-RecombDNA-L.jpg

12-12-RecombDNA-NL.jpg

12-13-DNAfinger-L.jpg

12-13-DNAfinger-NL.jpg

12-14-DNAforensics.jpg

12-15-PCR-L.jpg

12-15-PCR-NL.jpg

12-16-RestrctFrag-L.jpg

12-16-RestrctFrag-NL.jpg

12-17-RFLP-L.jpg

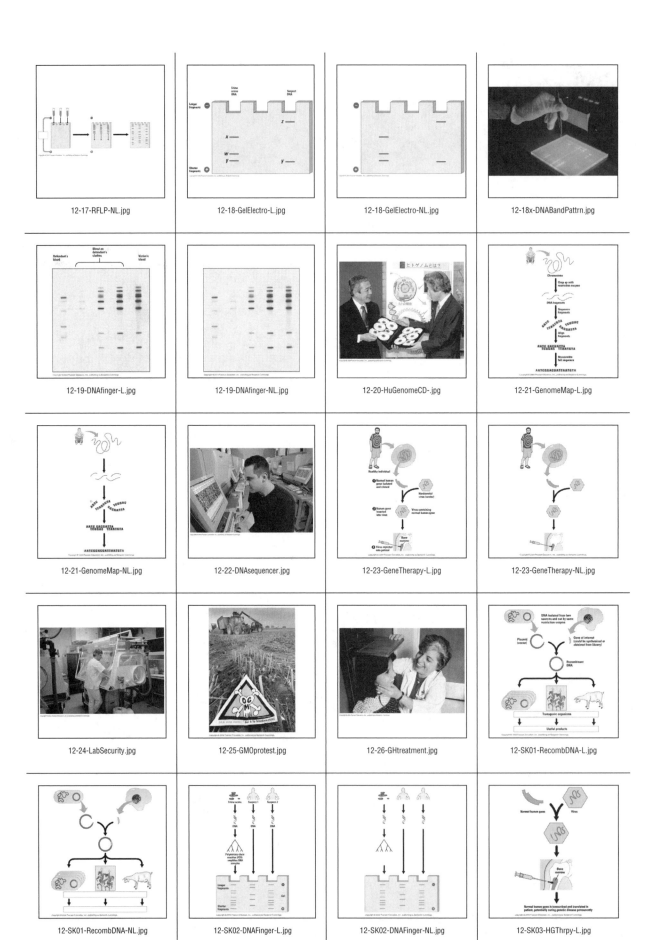

12-17-RFLP-NL.jpg

12-18-GelElectro-L.jpg

12-18-GelElectro-NL.jpg

12-18x-DNABandPattrn.jpg

12-19-DNAfinger-L.jpg

12-19-DNAfinger-NL.jpg

12-20-HuGenomeCD-.jpg

12-21-GenomeMap-L.jpg

12-21-GenomeMap-NL.jpg

12-22-DNAsequencer.jpg

12-23-GeneTherapy-L.jpg

12-23-GeneTherapy-NL.jpg

12-24-LabSecurity.jpg

12-25-GMOprotest.jpg

12-26-GHtreatment.jpg

12-SK01-RecombDNA-L.jpg

12-SK01-RecombDNA-NL.jpg

12-SK02-DNAFinger-L.jpg

12-SK02-DNAFinger-NL.jpg

12-SK03-HGThrpy-L.jpg

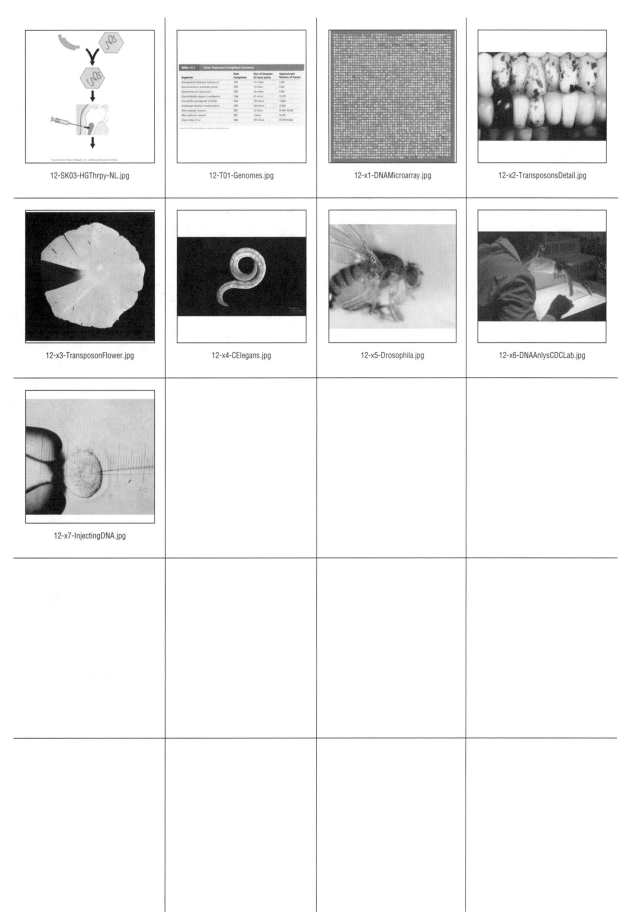

12-SK03-HGThrpy-NL.jpg

12-T01-Genomes.jpg

12-x1-DNAMicroarray.jpg

12-x2-TransposonsDetail.jpg

12-x3-TransposonFlower.jpg

12-x4-CElegans.jpg

12-x5-Drosophila.jpg

12-x6-DNAAnlysCDCLab.jpg

12-x7-InjectingDNA.jpg

13-00a-HumDiversity.jpg

13-00b-Antibiotics.jpg

13-00c-Homology.jpg

13-00d-Darwin.jpg

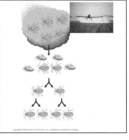

13-01-Insecticide-L.jpg

13-01-Insecticide-NL.jpg

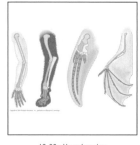

13-01x1-Darwin1859.jpg

13-01x2a-Darwin1874.jpg

13-01x2b-Darwin1874.jpg

13-01x3-DarwinCartn.jpg

13-01x4-Lamarck.jpg

13-01x5-Lyell.jpg

13-01x6-AlfredWallace.jpg

13-01x7-OrigOfSpecies.jpg

13-01x8-GeorgeCuvr.jpg

13-02a-InsectMimicry.jpg

13-02b-Camouflage.jpg

13-02c-Mimicry.jpg

13-03-BeagleVoyag-L.jpg

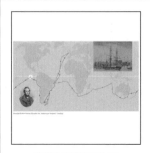

13-03-BeagleVoyag-NL.jpg

13-04-GalapagosVideo-B.mov

13-04-GalapagosVideo-S.mov

13-04-MarIguanaVideo-B.mov

13-04-MarIguanaVideo-S.mov

13-04-MarineIguana.jpg

13-04-SeaLionVideo-B.mov

13-04-SeaLionVideo-S.mov

13-04-TortoiseVideo-B.mov

13-04-TortoiseVideo-S.mov

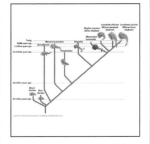

13-05-ElephPhylo-L.jpg

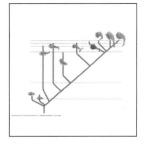

13-05-ElephPhylo-NL.jpg

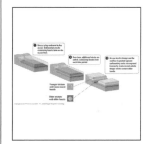

13-06-FormFossil-L.jpg

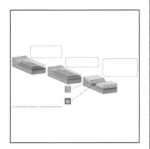

13-06-FormFossil-NL.jpg

13-07-GrndCanVideo-B.mov

13-07-GrndCanVideo-S.mov

13-07-SedStrata.jpg

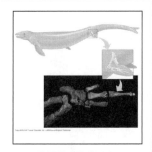

13-08-WhaleHindLimb.jpg

13-09-Biogeograph-L.jpg

13-09-Biogeograph-NL.jpg

13-09A-Koala-L.jpg

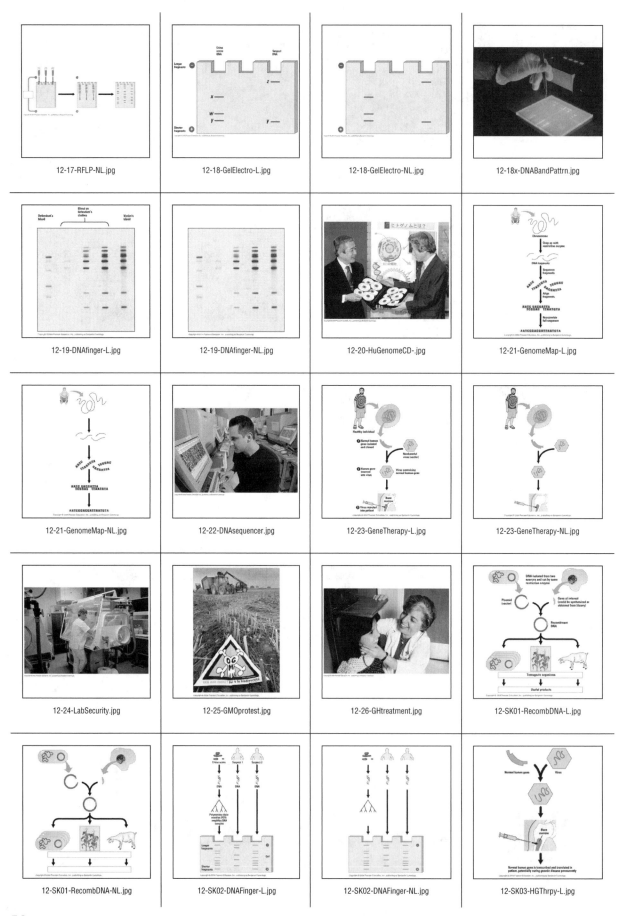

12-17-RFLP-NL.jpg

12-18-GelElectro-L.jpg

12-18-GelElectro-NL.jpg

12-18x-DNABandPattrn.jpg

12-19-DNAfinger-L.jpg

12-19-DNAfinger-NL.jpg

12-20-HuGenomeCD-.jpg

12-21-GenomeMap-L.jpg

12-21-GenomeMap-NL.jpg

12-22-DNAsequencer.jpg

12-23-GeneTherapy-L.jpg

12-23-GeneTherapy-NL.jpg

12-24-LabSecurity.jpg

12-25-GMOprotest.jpg

12-26-GHtreatment.jpg

12-SK01-RecombDNA-L.jpg

12-SK01-RecombDNA-NL.jpg

12-SK02-DNAFinger-L.jpg

12-SK02-DNAFinger-NL.jpg

12-SK03-HGThrpy-L.jpg

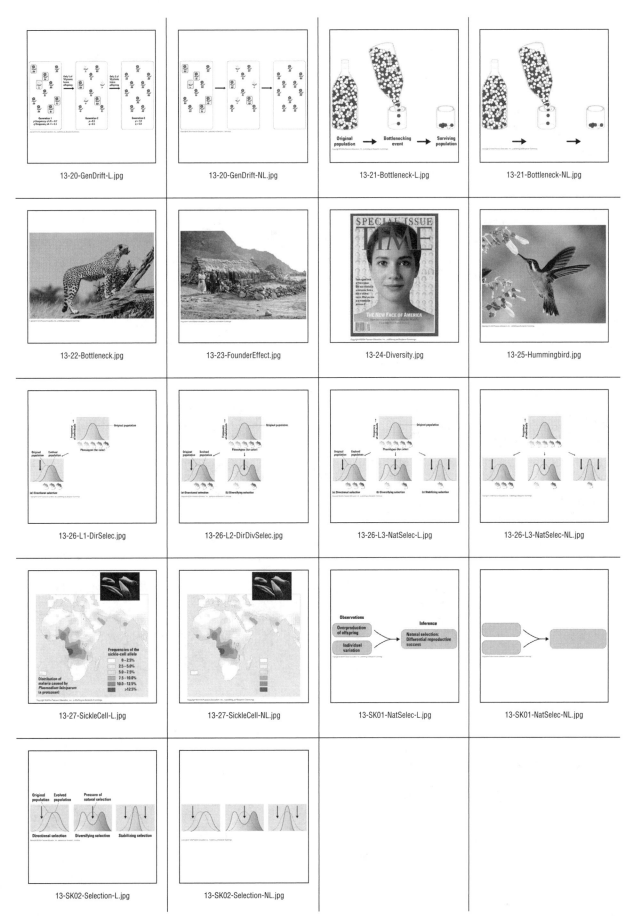

13-20-GenDrift-L.jpg

13-20-GenDrift-NL.jpg

13-21-Bottleneck-L.jpg

13-21-Bottleneck-NL.jpg

13-22-Bottleneck.jpg

13-23-FounderEffect.jpg

13-24-Diversity.jpg

13-25-Hummingbird.jpg

13-26-L1-DirSelec.jpg

13-26-L2-DirDivSelec.jpg

13-26-L3-NatSelec-L.jpg

13-26-L3-NatSelec-NL.jpg

13-27-SickleCell-L.jpg

13-27-SickleCell-NL.jpg

13-SK01-NatSelec-L.jpg

13-SK01-NatSelec-NL.jpg

13-SK02-Selection-L.jpg

13-SK02-Selection-NL.jpg

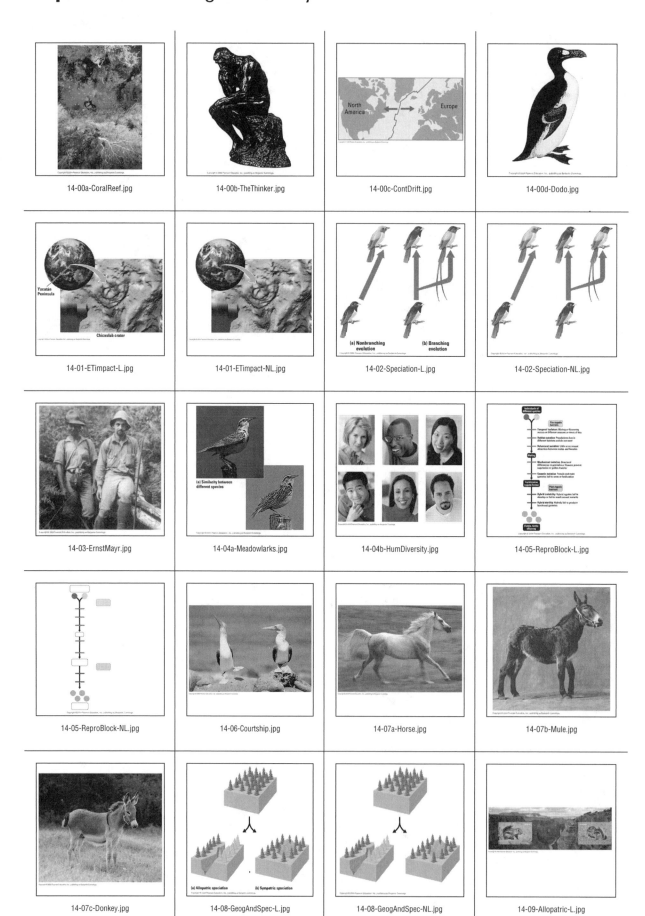

14-00a-CoralReef.jpg

14-00b-TheThinker.jpg

14-00c-ContDrift.jpg

14-00d-Dodo.jpg

14-01-ETimpact-L.jpg

14-01-ETimpact-NL.jpg

14-02-Speciation-L.jpg

14-02-Speciation-NL.jpg

14-03-ErnstMayr.jpg

14-04a-Meadowlarks.jpg

14-04b-HumDiversity.jpg

14-05-ReproBlock-L.jpg

14-05-ReproBlock-NL.jpg

14-06-Courtship.jpg

14-07a-Horse.jpg

14-07b-Mule.jpg

14-07c-Donkey.jpg

14-08-GeogAndSpec-L.jpg

14-08-GeogAndSpec-NL.jpg

14-09-Allopatric-L.jpg

14-09-Allopatric-NL.jpg

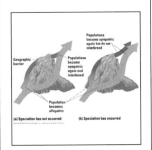

14-10-AllopatSpec-L.jpg

14-10-AllopatSpec-NL.jpg

14-11-HugodeVries.jpg

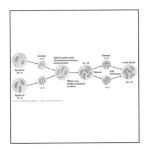

14-12-Polyploidy-L.jpg

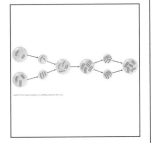

14-12-Polyploidy-NL.jpg

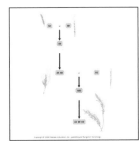

14-13-WheatEvol-L.jpg

14-13-WheatEvol-NL.jpg

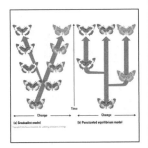

14-14-TempoOfEvol-L.jpg

14-14-TempoOfEvol-NL.jpg

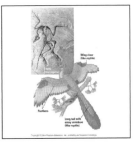

14-15-Archaeopter-L.jpg

14-15-Archaeopter-NL.jpg

14-16-Paedomorphosis.jpg

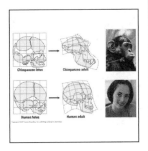

14-17-Paedomorph-L.jpg

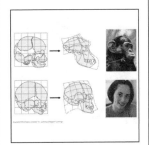

14-17-Paedomorph-NL.jpg

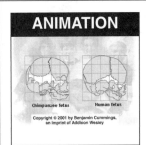

14-17-PaedomorphAnim.mov

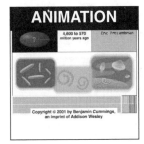

14-18-GeolTimScalAnim.mov

14-18a-DinosaurBone.jpg

14-18b-AfricanusSkul.jpg

14-18c-PetrifiedTree.jpg

14-18d-FossilLeaf.jpg

14-18e-Ammonites.jpg

14-18f-TraceFossils.jpg

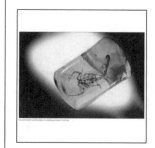

14-18g-InsectAmber.jpg

14-18h-FossilTusks.jpg

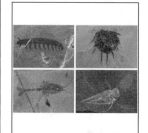

14-18x-BurgessShaleCollage.jpg

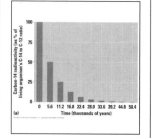

14-19a-C14Dating-.jpg

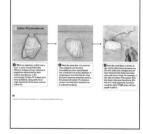

14-19b-ClamFossil-L.jpg

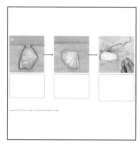

14-19b-ClamFossil-NL.jpg

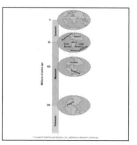

14-20-ContDrift-L.jpg

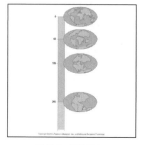

14-20-ContDrift-NL.jpg

14-20-LavaFlowVideo-B.mov

14-20-LavaFlowVideo-S.mov

14-20-VolcErptVideo-B.mov

14-20-VolcErptVideo-S.mov

14-20Ax-PlateBoundars.jpg

14-20Ax-SanAndreasFalt.jpg

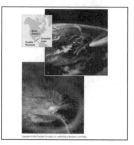

14-21-ETimpact-L.jpg

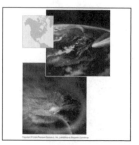

14-21-ETimpact-NL.jpg

14-21A-NorthAmer-L.jpg

14-21A-NorthAmer-NL.jpg

14-21B-Comet.jpg

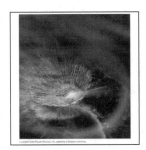
14-21C-Impact.jpg

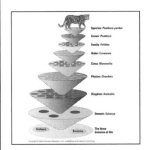
14-22-Taxonomy-L.jpg

14-22-Taxonomy-NL.jpg

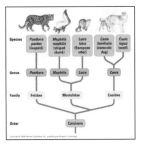
14-23-CarnPhylo-L.jpg

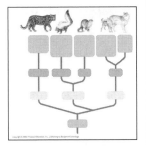
14-23-CarnPhylo-NL.jpg

14-24-TyroleanIceMan.jpg

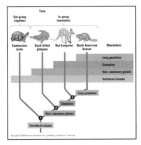
14-25-Cladistics-L.jpg

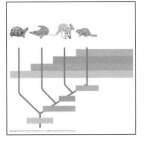
14-25-Cladistics-NL.jpg

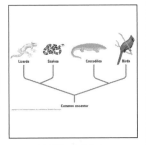
14-26-BirdCladist-L.jpg

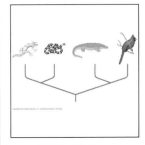
14-26-BirdCladist-NL.jpg

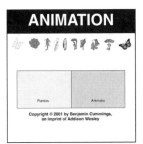
14-27-ClassificAnim.mov

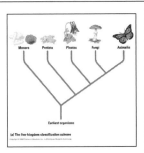
14-27a-5Kingdoms-L.jpg

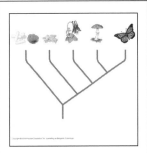
14-27a-5Kingdoms-NL.jpg

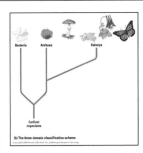
14-27b-3Domains-L.jpg

14-27b-3Domains-NL.jpg

14-SK01-Barriers-L.jpg

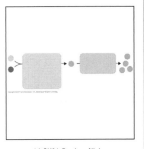
14-SK01-Barriers-NL.jpg

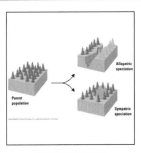
14-SK02-TreeSpec-L.jpg

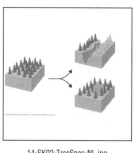

14-SK02-TreeSpec-NL.jpg

14-SK03-5Kingdom-L.jpg

14-SK03-5Kingdom-NL.jpg

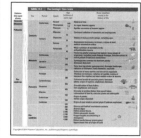

14-T01-GeolTimeScale.jpg

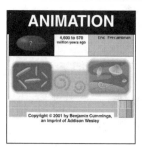

14-T01-GeolTmSclAnim.mov

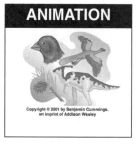

14-T01-MacroevoAnim.mov

14x1-FoxInSnow.jpg

14x2-HarborSeal.jpg

Chapter 15 The Evolution of Microbial Life

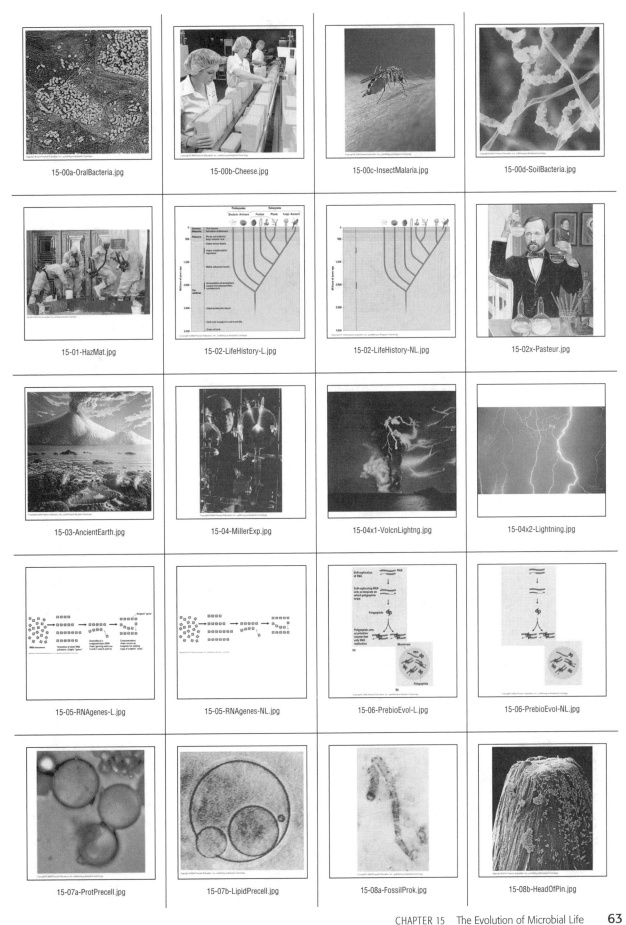

15-00a-OralBacteria.jpg

15-00b-Cheese.jpg

15-00c-InsectMalaria.jpg

15-00d-SoilBacteria.jpg

15-01-HazMat.jpg

15-02-LifeHistory-L.jpg

15-02-LifeHistory-NL.jpg

15-02x-Pasteur.jpg

15-03-AncientEarth.jpg

15-04-MillerExp.jpg

15-04x1-VolcnLightng.jpg

15-04x2-Lightning.jpg

15-05-RNAgenes-L.jpg

15-05-RNAgenes-NL.jpg

15-06-PrebioEvol-L.jpg

15-06-PrebioEvol-NL.jpg

15-07a-ProtPrecell.jpg

15-07b-LipidPrecell.jpg

15-08a-FossilProk.jpg

15-08b-HeadOfPin.jpg

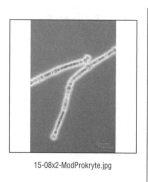

15-08x1-EarlyModProk.jpg

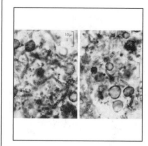

15-08x2-ModProkryte.jpg

15-08x3-FilaProkFossl.jpg

15-08x4-UniceProkFos.jpg

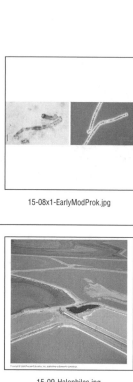

15-09-Halophiles.jpg

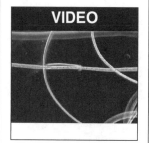

15-10a-Cocci.jpg

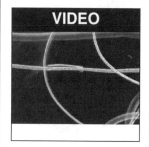

15-10b-Bacilli.jpg

15-10c-Spitochetes.jpg

15-10x-BeggiaSulfEat.jpg

15-11-OscillaVideo-B.mov

15-11-OscillaVideo-S.mov

15-11a-Actinomycete.jpg

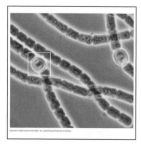

15-11b-Cyanobacteria.jpg

15-11c-GiantBact.jpg

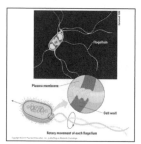

15-12-ProkFlag-L.jpg

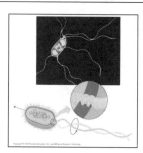

15-12-ProkFlag-NL.jpg

15-12-SalFlagVideo-S.mov

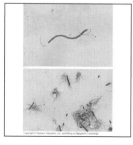

15-12x-ProkFlagCol.jpg

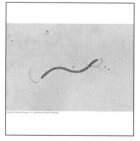

15-12x1-TwoProkFlag.jpg

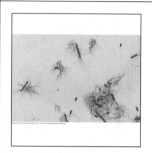

15-12x2-MnyProkFlag.jpg

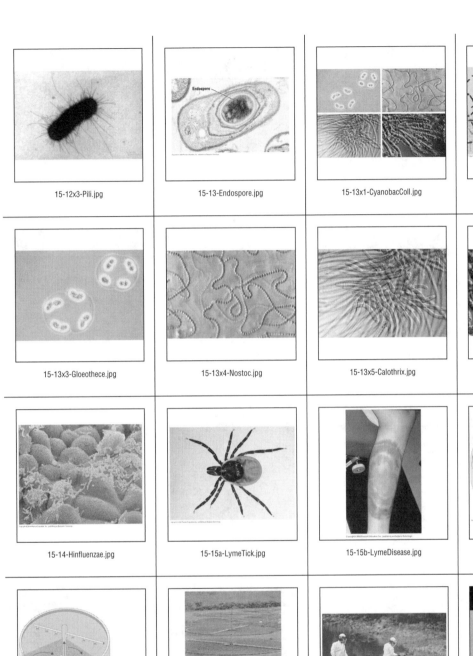

15-12x3-Pili.jpg

15-13-Endospore.jpg

15-13x1-CyanobacColl.jpg

15-13x2-Endospores.jpg

15-13x3-Gloeothece.jpg

15-13x4-Nostoc.jpg

15-13x5-Calothrix.jpg

15-13x6-Fischerella.jpg

15-14-Hinfluenzae.jpg

15-15a-LymeTick.jpg

15-15b-LymeDisease.jpg

15-16-1-SwgeTreat-L.jpg

15-16-1-SwgeTreat-NL.jpg

15-16-2-ProkAndSewag.jpg

15-17-OilSpillTreat.jpg

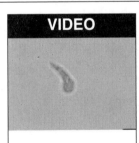

15-18-Euglna1Video-B.mov

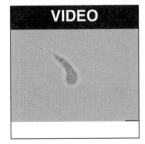

15-18-Euglna1Video-S.mov

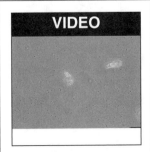

15-18-Euglna2Video-B.mov

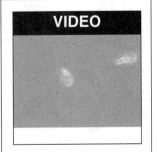

15-18-Euglna2Video-S.mov

15-18-EukEvol-L.jpg

15-18-EukEvol-NL.jpg

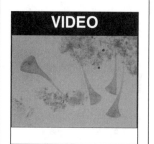

15-19-Stent1Video-B.mov

15-19-Stent1Video-S.mov

15-19-Stent2Video-B.mov

15-19-Stent2Video-S.mov

15-19-Vortic1Video-B.mov

15-19-Vortic1Video-S.mov

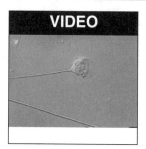

15-19-Vortic2Video-B.mov

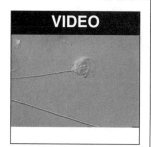

15-19-Vortic2Video-S.mov

15-19-Vortic3Video-B.mov

15-19-Vortic3Video-S.mov

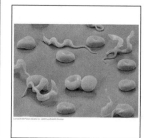

15-19a-Trypanosomes.jpg

15-19b-Amoeba-L.jpg

15-19b-Amoeba-NL.jpg

15-19b-AmoPs1Video-B.mov

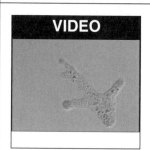

15-19b-AmoPs1Video-S.mov

15-19b-AmoPs2Video-B.mov

15-19b-AmoPs2Video-S.mov

15-19c-Foram.jpg

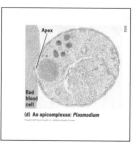

15-19d-Plasmodm-L.jpg

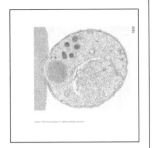

15-19d-Plasmodm-NL.jpg

15-19e-Paramecm-L.jpg

15-19e-Paramecm-NL.jpg

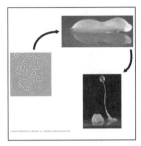

15-19x-Protists.jpg

15-20-PlasSlimeMold.jpg

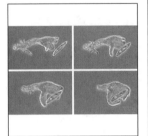

15-20x-PseudopdiaCol.jpg

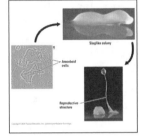

15-21-SlimeMold-L.jpg

15-21-SlimeMold-NL.jpg

15-21-SlmeMldVideo-B.mov

15-21-SlmeMldVideo-S.mov

15-21-SlmMoStVideo-B.mov

15-21-SlmMoStVideo-S.mov

15-21x-DictystelmCol.jpg

15-21x-SlmeMoldSpor.jpg

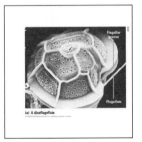

15-22a-Dinoflagell.jpg

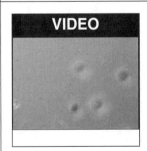

15-22A-DinoflVideo-B.mov

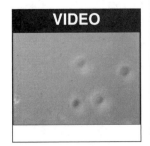

15-22A-DinoflVideo-S.mov

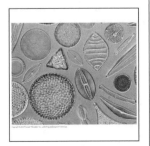

15-22b-Diatoms.jpg

15-22B-MiDia1Video-B.mov

15-22B-MiDia1Video-S.mov

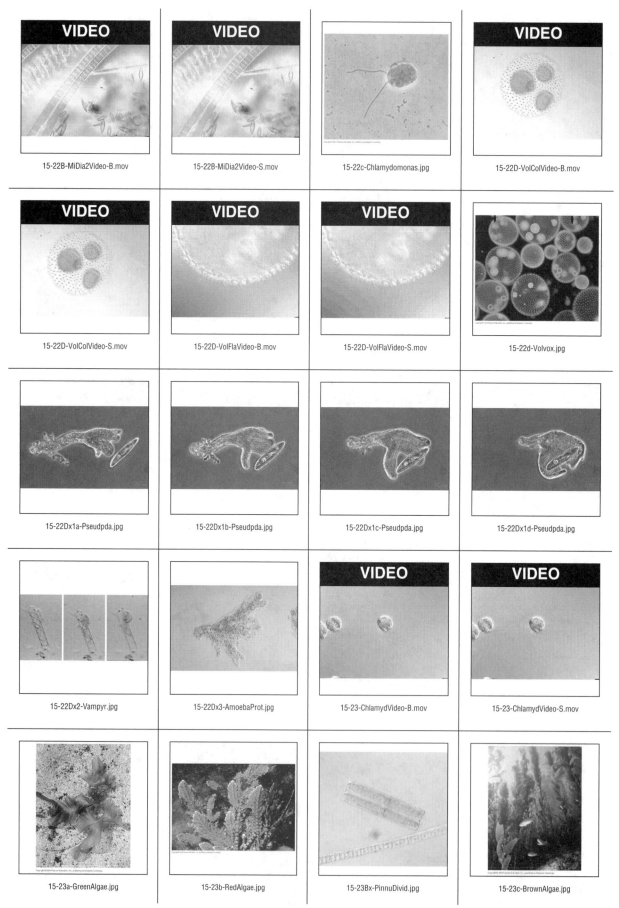

15-22B-MiDia2Video-B.mov

15-22B-MiDia2Video-S.mov

15-22c-Chlamydomonas.jpg

15-22D-VolColVideo-B.mov

15-22D-VolColVideo-S.mov

15-22D-VolFlaVideo-B.mov

15-22D-VolFlaVideo-S.mov

15-22d-Volvox.jpg

15-22Dx1a-Pseudpda.jpg

15-22Dx1b-Pseudpda.jpg

15-22Dx1c-Pseudpda.jpg

15-22Dx1d-Pseudpda.jpg

15-22Dx2-Vampyr.jpg

15-22Dx3-AmoebaProt.jpg

15-23-ChlamydVideo-B.mov

15-23-ChlamydVideo-S.mov

15-23a-GreenAlgae.jpg

15-23b-RedAlgae.jpg

15-23Bx-PinnuDivid.jpg

15-23c-BrownAlgae.jpg

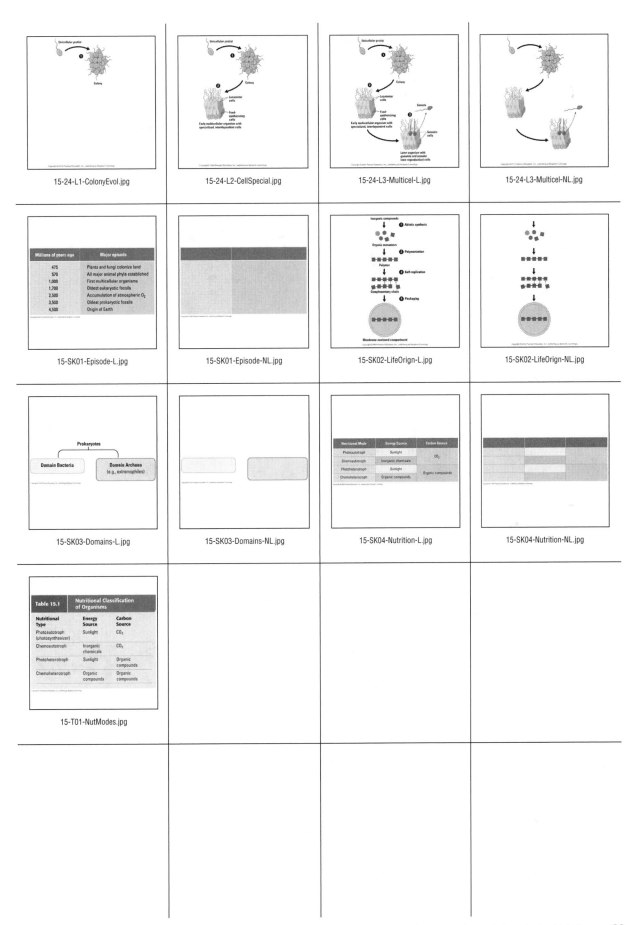

15-24-L1-ColonyEvol.jpg

15-24-L2-CellSpecial.jpg

15-24-L3-Multicel-L.jpg

15-24-L3-Multicel-NL.jpg

15-SK01-Episode-L.jpg

15-SK01-Episode-NL.jpg

15-SK02-LifeOrign-L.jpg

15-SK02-LifeOrign-NL.jpg

15-SK03-Domains-L.jpg

15-SK03-Domains-NL.jpg

15-SK04-Nutrition-L.jpg

15-SK04-Nutrition-NL.jpg

15-T01-NutModes.jpg

16-00a-Sequoia.jpg

16-00b-Mushrooms.jpg

16-00c-Crops.jpg

16-00d-RainForest.jpg

16-01-ClearCutTree.jpg

16-02-PltTimeVideo-B.mov

16-02-PltTimeVideo-S.mov

16-02-TerresAdapt-L.jpg

16-02-TerresAdapt-NL.jpg

16-03-Mycorrhizae-L.jpg

16-03-Mycorrhizae-NL.jpg

16-03x-Mycorrhizae.jpg

16-04-Leaf.jpg

16-05-Embryo-L.jpg

16-05-Embryo-NL.jpg

16-06a-Chara.jpg

16-06b-Coleochaete.jpg

16-06x-Chara2.jpg

16-07-PlantPhylo-L.jpg

16-07-PlantPhylo-NL.jpg

16-08-PeatMossBog.jpg

16-09-Moss-L.jpg

Spore capsule

Sporophyte

Gametophytes

16-09-Moss-NL.jpg

16-09x1-MossLifeCycle.jpg

16-09x1a-MossGameto.jpg

16-09x1b-MossArcheg.jpg

16-09x1c-MossSporo.jpg

16-09x1d-MossSporang.jpg

16-09x1e-MossSpores.jpg

16-09x1f-MosProtnemta.jpg

16-09x2-MosSporang.jpg

16-09x3-SphagnumMoss.jpg

16-09x4-SphagnumLeaf.jpg

16-09x5-LeafyLivrwrt.jpg

16-09x6-ThalldLivrwrt.jpg

16-09x7-Hornwort.jpg

16-10-L1-PlantSpores.jpg

16-10-L2-Gametes.jpg

16-10-L3-AltOfGen-L.jpg

16-10-L3-AltOfGen-NL.jpg

ANIMATION

16-10-MossLfCycAnim.mov

16-11-Ferns.jpg

ANIMATION

16-11-FrnLfeCycAnim.mov

16-11A-Spores.jpg

16-11B-Forest.jpg

16-11C-Fiddlehead.jpg

16-11x1-MatureFern.jpg

16-11x2-FernSorus.jpg

16-11x3-FernSporan.jpg

16-11x4-FernOldSporn.jpg

16-11x5-FernGermin.jpg

16-11x6-FernGametph.jpg

16-11x7-FernArchegn.jpg

16-11x8-FernSporo.jpg

16-11x9-FernSpore.jpg

16-12-CoalForest.jpg

16-13-PeytoLake.jpg

16-13x-DouglasFir.jpg

16-13x1-FrasierFir.jpg

16-14-AltOfGen-L.jpg

16-14-AltOfGen-NL.jpg

16-15-PineLfCycAnim.mov

16-15-PineTree.jpg

16-15x2-MalePinePoll.jpg

16-15x3-PinePollnCon.jpg

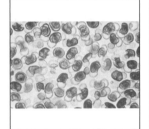

16-15x4a-PinePollen.jpg

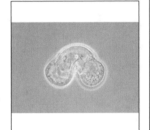

16-15x4b-PinPollSin.jpg

16-15x5-FemPineCone.jpg

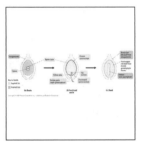

16-16-OvuleToSeed-L.jpg

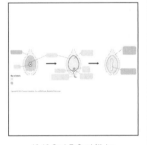

16-16-OvuleToSeed-NL.jpg

16-16x6-PineOvulatCn.jpg

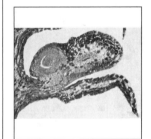

16-16x7a-PineOvule.jpg

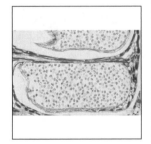

16-16x7b-PineSporan.jpg

16-16x8-PineEmbryo.jpg

16-17-BatPoVideo-B.mov

16-17-BatPoVideo-S.mov

16-17-BeePoVideo-B.mov

16-17-BeePoVideo-S.mov

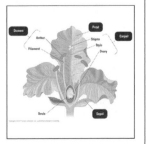

16-17-Flower-L.jpg

16-17-Flower-NL.jpg

VIDEO	VIDEO		
16-17-FlwTimVideo-B.mov	16-17-FlwTimVideo-S.mov	16-18-AngioCycle-L.jpg	16-18-AngioCycle-NL.jpg

16-18x-PolGrainSEM.jpg	16-19a-Dandelion.jpg	16-19b-Cockleburs.jpg	16-19c-FruitMouse.jpg

16-19x-Botrytis.jpg	16-19x1-Deforesta.jpg	16-19x1-PineSdDispl.jpg	16-19x2-DisperColl.jpg

16-19x2-SlashBurn.jpg	16-19x3-PineFarm.jpg	VIDEO 16-20-ErthwrmVideo-B.mov	VIDEO 16-20-ErthwrmVideo-S.mov

16-20a-FlyAgaricMush.jpg	16-20b-FairyRing.jpg	16-20c-Pilobolus.jpg	16-20cx-Pilobolus.jpg

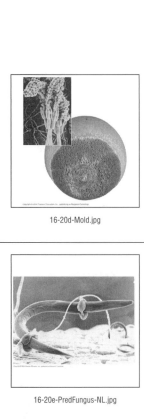

16-20d-Mold.jpg

16-20dx-HyphaeColl.jpg

16-20dx1-SoilPlate.jpg

16-20e-PredFungus-L.jpg

16-20e-PredFungus-NL.jpg

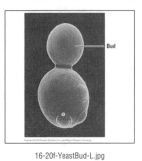

16-20f-YeastBud-L.jpg

16-20f-YeastBud-NL.jpg

16-20x-MoldyOrngeCol.jpg

16-20x1-MoldyOrange.jpg

16-20x10-Aspergillus.jpg

16-20x11-GillsBasidCol.jpg

16-20x11a-Gills.jpg

16-20x12b-GillBasidLM.jpg

16-20x2-Penicillium.jpg

16-20x3-Amanita.jpg

16-20x4-Coprinus.jpg

16-20x5-GrevilBolete.jpg

16-20x6-Morel.jpg

16-20x7-Stinkhorn.jpg

16-20x8-Trametes.jpg

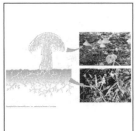
16-20x9-Tremella.jpg

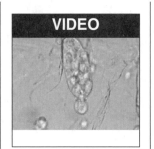
16-21-AlmyZooVideo-S.mov

16-21-FungLfeCycAnim.mov

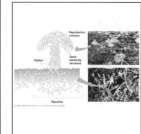
16-21-Mycelium-L.jpg

16-21-Mycelium-NL.jpg

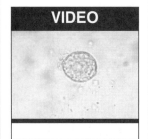
16-21-PhlyZooVideo-B.mov

16-21-PhlyZooVideo-S.mov

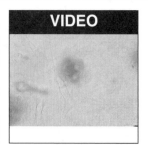
16-21-SapOogoVideo-B.mov

16-21-SapOogoVideo-S.mov

16-21-SapZooVideo-B.mov

16-21-SapZooVideo-S.mov

16-22a-DutchElmDis.jpg

16-22b-ErgotsRye.jpg

16-23a-Truffles.jpg

16-23b-BlueCheese.jpg

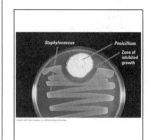
16-24-Penicillium-L.jpg

16-24-Penicillium-NL.jpg

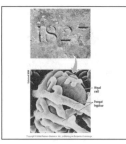
16-25-Lichens-L.jpg

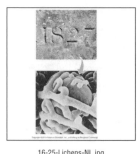
16-25-Lichens-NL.jpg

16-25x-LichenAnat.jpg

16-38-FlpGeesVideo-B.mov

16-38-FlpGeesVideo-S.mov

16-38-HawkVideo-B.mov

16-38-HawkVideo-S.mov

16-38-SwanFltVideo-B.mov

16-38-SwanFltVideo-S.mov

16-SK01-TerrPlnts-L.jpg

16-SK01-TerrPlnts-NL.jpg

16-SK02-PlantEvol-L.jpg

16-SK02-PlantEvol-NL.jpg

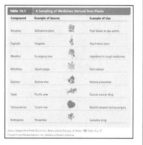

16-T01-MedFromPlant.jpg

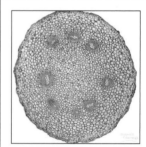

16x1-PolypodmStem.jpg

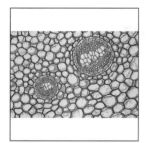

16x2-PhloemXylem.jpg

16x3-Lycophyte.jpg

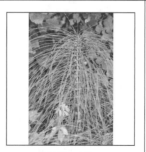

16x4-Horsetail.jpg

16x5-Septate.jpg

16x6-Nonseptate.jpg

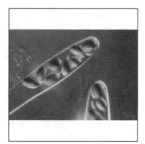

16x7-MatureAsci.jpg

16x8-Apothecium.jpg

Chapter 17 The Evolution of Animals

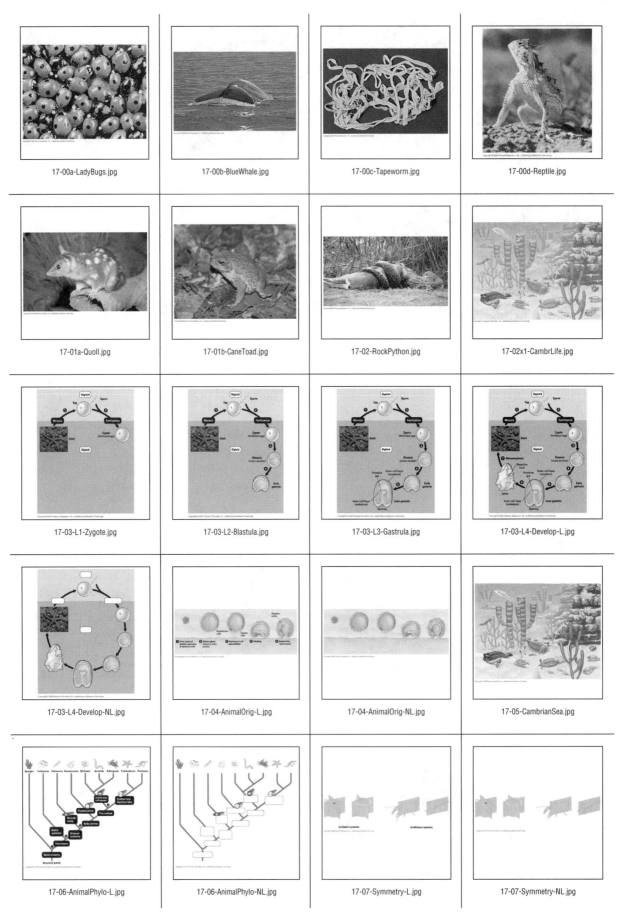

17-00a-LadyBugs.jpg

17-00b-BlueWhale.jpg

17-00c-Tapeworm.jpg

17-00d-Reptile.jpg

17-01a-Quoll.jpg

17-01b-CaneToad.jpg

17-02-RockPython.jpg

17-02x1-CambrLife.jpg

17-03-L1-Zygote.jpg

17-03-L2-Blastula.jpg

17-03-L3-Gastrula.jpg

17-03-L4-Develop-L.jpg

17-03-L4-Develop-NL.jpg

17-04-AnimalOrig-L.jpg

17-04-AnimalOrig-NL.jpg

17-05-CambrianSea.jpg

17-06-AnimalPhylo-L.jpg

17-06-AnimalPhylo-NL.jpg

17-07-Symmetry-L.jpg

17-07-Symmetry-NL.jpg

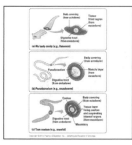

17-08-BodyPlans-L.jpg

17-08-BodyPlans-NL.jpg

17-09-Sponge.jpg

17-09Dx-Sponges.jpg

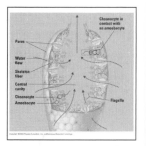

17-10-Sponge-L.jpg

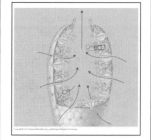

17-10-Sponge-NL.jpg

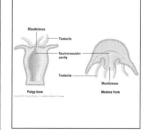

17-11-Cnidaria-L.jpg

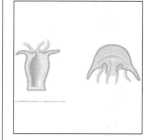

17-11-Cnidaria-NL.jpg

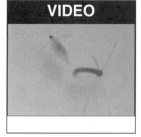

17-11-HydrEatVideo-B.mov

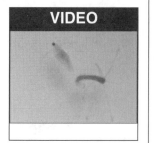

17-11-HydrEatVideo-S.mov

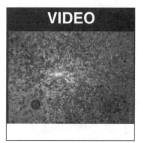

17-11-ThmbJelVideo-B.mov

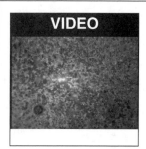

17-11-ThmbJelVideo-S.mov

17-11A-HySperVideo-B.mov

17-11A-HySperVideo-S.mov

17-11a-SeaAnemone.jpg

17-11Ax-CorlPolyps.jpg

17-11Ax-SeaAnem.jpg

17-11B-JelSwmVideo-B.mov

17-11B-JelSwmVideo-S.mov

17-11b-Medusa.jpg

17-11Bx1-PurpStrpJel.jpg

17-11Bx2-LionMnJelly.jpg

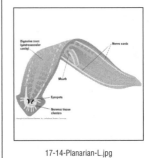

17-11x1-Cnidarians.jpg

Ctenophore image

17-11x2-Ctenophore.jpg

Coral image

17-12-Coral.jpg

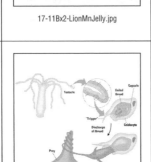

17-13-Cnidocyte-L.jpg

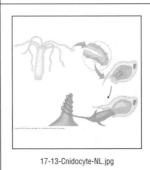

17-13-Cnidocyte-NL.jpg

Planarian image

17-14-Planarian-L.jpg

17-14-Planarian-NL.jpg

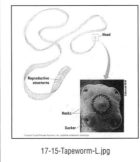

17-15-Tapeworm-L.jpg

17-15-Tapeworm-NL.jpg

Flatworm image

17-15x-Flatworm.jpg

VIDEO

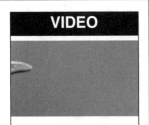

17-16-CelegCraVideo-B.mov

VIDEO

17-16-CelegCraVideo-S.mov

VIDEO

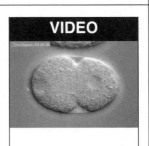

17-16-CelegDevVideo-S.mov

Roundworm image

17-16a-Roundworm.jpg

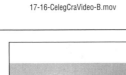

17-16ax-NematCElegans.jpg

Trichinell image

17-16b-Trichinell-L.jpg

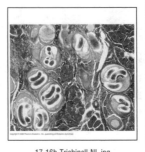

17-16b-Trichinell-NL.jpg

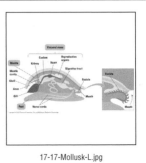

17-17-Mollusk-L.jpg

17-17-Mollusk-NL.jpg

17-18-SeaSlugVideo-B.mov

17-18-SeaSlugVideo-S.mov

17-18a-Gastropods.jpg

17-18b-Scallop.jpg

17-18c-Octopus.jpg

17-18x-DeerCowrie.jpg

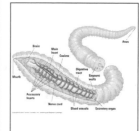
17-19-Earthworm-L.jpg

17-19-Earthworm-NL.jpg

17-19Ax-Earthworm.jpg

17-20a-BigEarthworm.jpg

17-20b1-Sandworm.jpg

17-20b2-FanWorm.jpg

17-20c-Leech.jpg

17-21-LobMthVideo-B.mov

17-21-LobMthVideo-S.mov

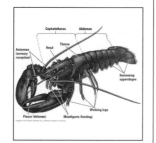
17-21-Lobster-L.jpg

17-21-Lobster-NL.jpg

17-22a-Scorpion.jpg

17-22b-Spider.jpg

17-22c-Mite.jpg

17-23a-Shrimp.jpg

17-23b-Barnacles.jpg

17-24-Millipede.jpg

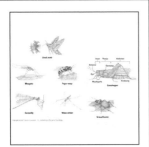

17-25-Insects-L.jpg

17-25-Insects-NL.jpg

17-25Dx-Beetle.jpg

17-26-ButflyVideo-B.mov

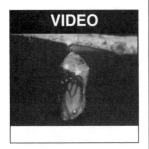

17-26-ButflyVideo-S.mov

17-26-Butterfly-L.jpg

17-26-Butterfly-NL.jpg

17-26Ex-Metamorphos.jpg

17-27-EchTbFtVideo-B.mov

17-27-EchTbFtVideo-S.mov

17-27a-1-SeaStar.jpg

17-27a-2-SeaStarPrey.jpg

17-27Ax1-Bloodstar.jpg

17-27Ax2-BrittleStar.jpg

17-27b-SeaUrchin.jpg

17-27c-SeaCucumber.jpg

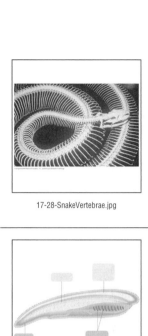

17-28-SnakeVertebrae.jpg

17-29a-Lancelet.jpg

17-29b-Tunicate.jpg

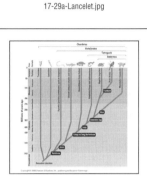

17-30-Chordate-L.jpg

17-30-Chordate-NL.jpg

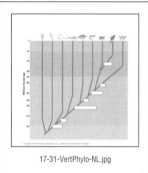

17-31-VertPhylo-L.jpg

17-31-VertPhylo-NL.jpg

17-32a-Cartilaginous.jpg

17-32A-MantaVideo-B.mov

17-32A-MantaVideo-S.mov

17-32Ax-CartilFishes.jpg

17-32b-BonyFish-L.jpg

17-32b-BonyFish-NL.jpg

17-33-Amphibian-L.jpg

17-33-Amphibian-NL.jpg

17-34-TetrapEvol-L.jpg

17-34-TetrapEvol-NL.jpg

17-35-BullSnake.jpg

17-35x1-ExtantReptile.jpg

17-35x1a-DsrtTortois.jpg

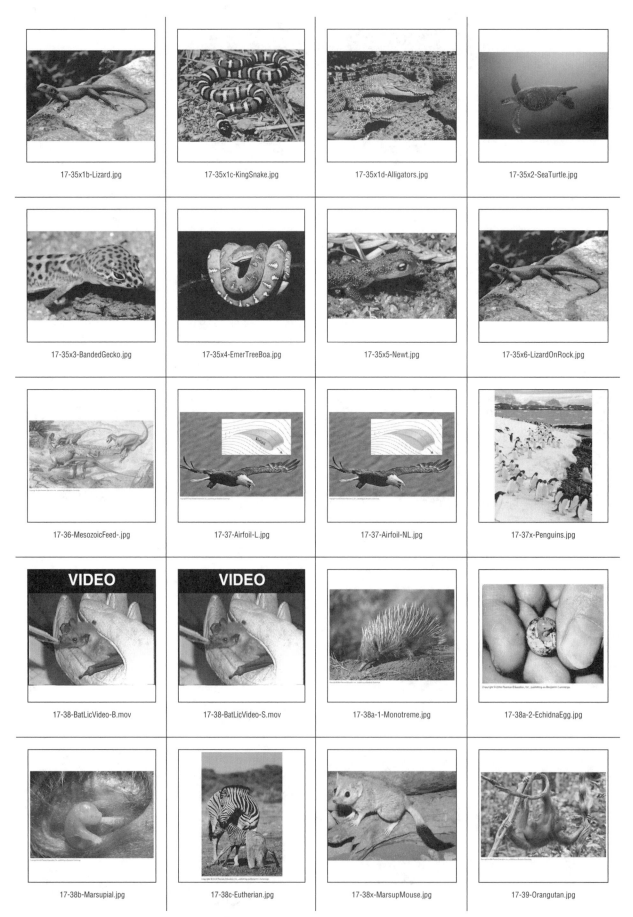

17-35x1b-Lizard.jpg

17-35x1c-KingSnake.jpg

17-35x1d-Alligators.jpg

17-35x2-SeaTurtle.jpg

17-35x3-BandedGecko.jpg

17-35x4-EmerTreeBoa.jpg

17-35x5-Newt.jpg

17-35x6-LizardOnRock.jpg

17-36-MesozoicFeed-.jpg

17-37-Airfoil-L.jpg

17-37-Airfoil-NL.jpg

17-37x-Penguins.jpg

17-38-BatLicVideo-B.mov

17-38-BatLicVideo-S.mov

17-38a-1-Monotreme.jpg

17-38a-2-EchidnaEgg.jpg

17-38b-Marsupial.jpg

17-38c-Eutherian.jpg

17-38x-MarsupMouse.jpg

17-39-Orangutan.jpg

17-40-GibbnVideo-B.mov

17-40-GibbnVideo-S.mov

17-40a-Prosimian.jpg

17-40b-SpiderMonkey.jpg

17-40c-Macaque.jpg

17-40d-Gibbon.jpg

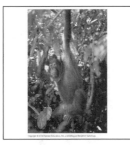

17-40e-Orangutan.jpg

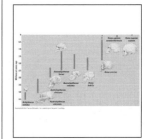

17-40f-Gorilla.jpg

17-40g-Chimpanzee.jpg

17-40h-Human.jpg

17-40x-ApesCollage.jpg

17-40x-OldNewMonkey.jpg

17-40x2-Lemurs.jpg

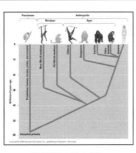

17-41-PrimatPhylo-L.jpg

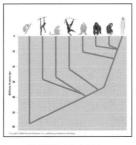

17-41-PrimatPhylo-NL.jpg

17-42-Hominids-L.jpg

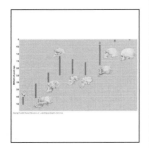

17-42-Hominids-NL.jpg

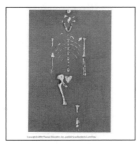

17-43a-Lucy.jpg

17-43b-Footprints.jpg

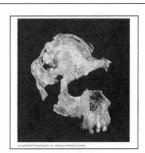

17-43c-AfarensisSkul.jpg

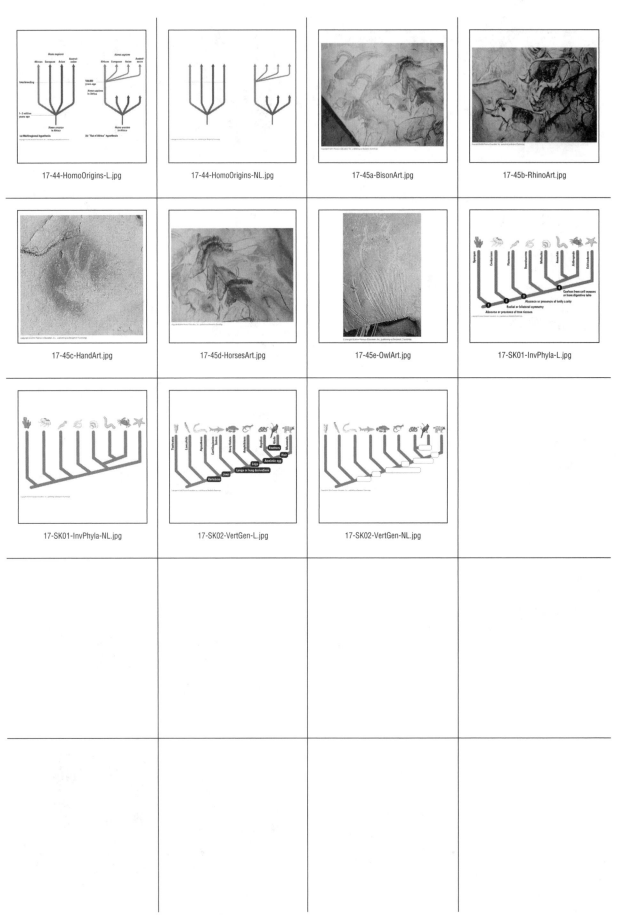

17-44-HomoOrigins-L.jpg

17-44-HomoOrigins-NL.jpg

17-45a-BisonArt.jpg

17-45b-RhinoArt.jpg

17-45c-HandArt.jpg

17-45d-HorsesArt.jpg

17-45e-OwlArt.jpg

17-SK01-InvPhyla-L.jpg

17-SK01-InvPhyla-NL.jpg

17-SK02-VertGen-L.jpg

17-SK02-VertGen-NL.jpg

Chapter 18 The Ecology of Organisms and Populations

18-00a-UrbanCrowd.jpg

18-00b-Bird.jpg

18-00C-ForestFire.jpg

18-00D-EverestSummit.jpg

18-01-ClearCutting.jpg

18-02a-ForestCanopy.jpg

18-02b-Grard.jpg

18-03-ExpEcology.jpg

18-04a-Organism.jpg

18-04b-Population.jpg

18-04c-Community.jpg

18-04d-Ecosystem.jpg

18-05-Carson.jpg

18-06-Protesters.jpg

18-07-GlobalProduct.jpg

18-08-Patchiness.jpg

18-09-HotProkPool.jpg

18-10-FlagTrees.jpg

18-11a-ForestFire.jpg

18-11b-2Succession.jpg

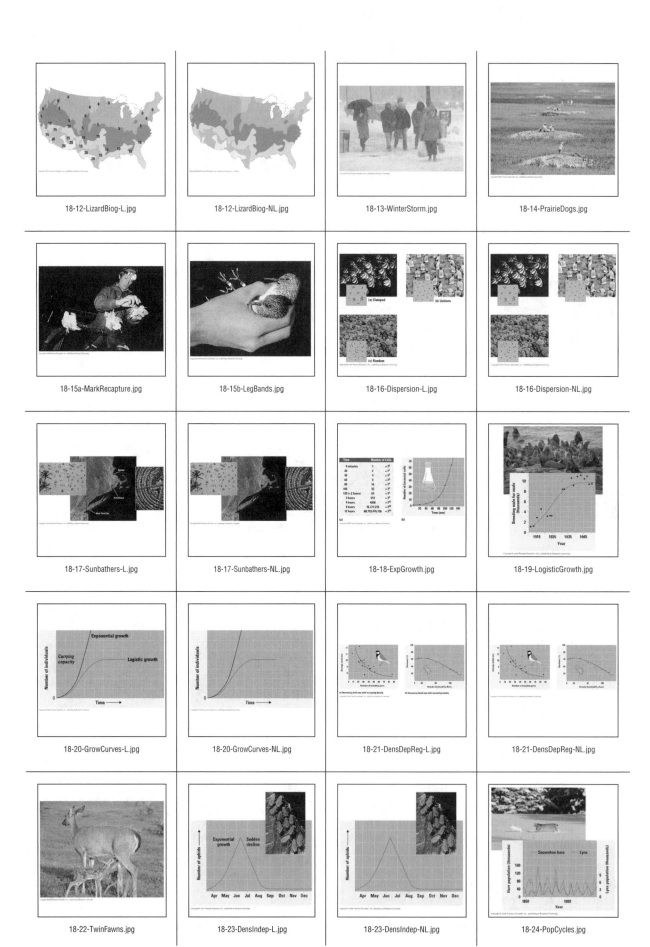

18-12-LizardBiog-L.jpg

18-12-LizardBiog-NL.jpg

18-13-WinterStorm.jpg

18-14-PrairieDogs.jpg

18-15a-MarkRecapture.jpg

18-15b-LegBands.jpg

18-16-Dispersion-L.jpg

18-16-Dispersion-NL.jpg

18-17-Sunbathers-L.jpg

18-17-Sunbathers-NL.jpg

18-18-ExpGrowth.jpg

18-19-LogisticGrowth.jpg

18-20-GrowCurves-L.jpg

18-20-GrowCurves-NL.jpg

18-21-DensDepReg-L.jpg

18-21-DensDepReg-NL.jpg

18-22-TwinFawns.jpg

18-23-DensIndep-L.jpg

18-23-DensIndep-NL.jpg

18-24-PopCycles.jpg

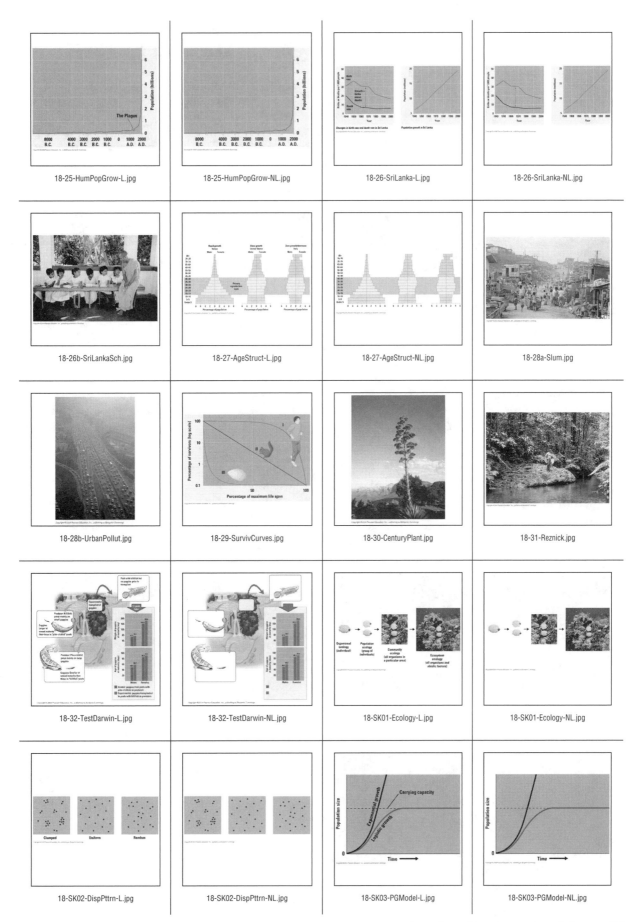

18-25-HumPopGrow-L.jpg

18-25-HumPopGrow-NL.jpg

18-26-SriLanka-L.jpg

18-26-SriLanka-NL.jpg

18-26b-SriLankaSch.jpg

18-27-AgeStruct-L.jpg

18-27-AgeStruct-NL.jpg

18-28a-Slum.jpg

18-28b-UrbanPollut.jpg

18-29-SurvivCurves.jpg

18-30-CenturyPlant.jpg

18-31-Reznick.jpg

18-32-TestDarwin-L.jpg

18-32-TestDarwin-NL.jpg

18-SK01-Ecology-L.jpg

18-SK01-Ecology-NL.jpg

18-SK02-DispPttrn-L.jpg

18-SK02-DispPttrn-NL.jpg

18-SK03-PGModel-L.jpg

18-SK03-PGModel-NL.jpg

18-T01-USlifeTable.jpg

18-T02-LifeHistories.jpg

18-x1-DuckIngVideo-B.mov

18-x1-DuckIngVideo-S.mov

18-x2-ChmpCrkVideo-B.mov

18-x2-ChmpCrkVideo-S.mov

18-x3-ChmpAgnVideo-B.mov

18-x3-ChmpAgnVideo-S.mov

18-x4-SnkWresVideo-B.mov

18-x4-SnkWresVideo-S.mov

18-x5-WolfAgnVideo-B.mov

18-x5-WolfAgnVideo-S.mov

18-x6-AlbaCrtVideo-B.mov

18-x6-AlbaCrtVideo-S.mov

18-x7-BobiCrtVideo-B.mov

18-x7-BobiCrtVideo-S.mov

18-x8-GirfCrtVideo-B.mov

18-x8-GirfCrtVideo-S.mov

Chapter 19 Communities and Ecosystems

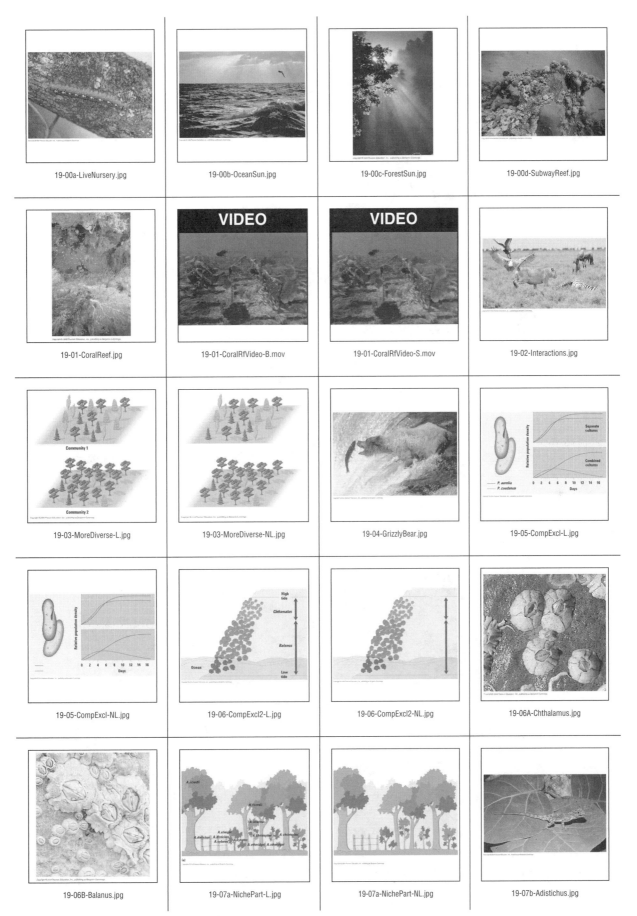

19-00a-LiveNursery.jpg

19-00b-OceanSun.jpg

19-00c-ForestSun.jpg

19-00d-SubwayReef.jpg

19-01-CoralReef.jpg

19-01-CoralRfVideo-B.mov

19-01-CoralRfVideo-S.mov

19-02-Interactions.jpg

19-03-MoreDiverse-L.jpg

19-03-MoreDiverse-NL.jpg

19-04-GrizzlyBear.jpg

19-05-CompExcl-L.jpg

19-05-CompExcl-NL.jpg

19-06-CompExcl2-L.jpg

19-06-CompExcl2-NL.jpg

19-06A-Chthalamus.jpg

19-06B-Balanus.jpg

19-07a-NichePart-L.jpg

19-07a-NichePart-NL.jpg

19-07b-Adistichus.jpg

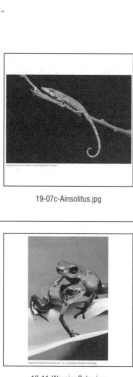

19-07c-Ainsolitus.jpg

19-08-Mobbing.jpg

19-09-ProtectYoung.jpg

19-10-Camouflage.jpg

19-11-WarningColor.jpg

19-12a-HawkMothLarva.jpg

19-12b-Batesian.jpg

19-13a-Mullerian.jpg

19-13b-YellowJacket.jpg

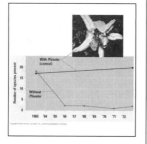

19-14-Keystone-L.jpg

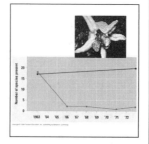

19-14-Keystone-NL.jpg

19-15-AustralRabbits.jpg

19-16-AcaciaAnts.jpg

19-16-FishAneVideo-B.mov

19-16-FishAneVideo-S.mov

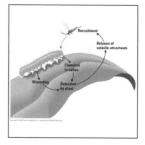

19-17-ComInteract-L.jpg

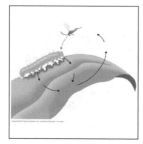

19-17-ComInteract-NL.jpg

19-18a-Glacier.jpg

19-18b-BarrenLand.jpg

19-18c-MossLichen.jpg

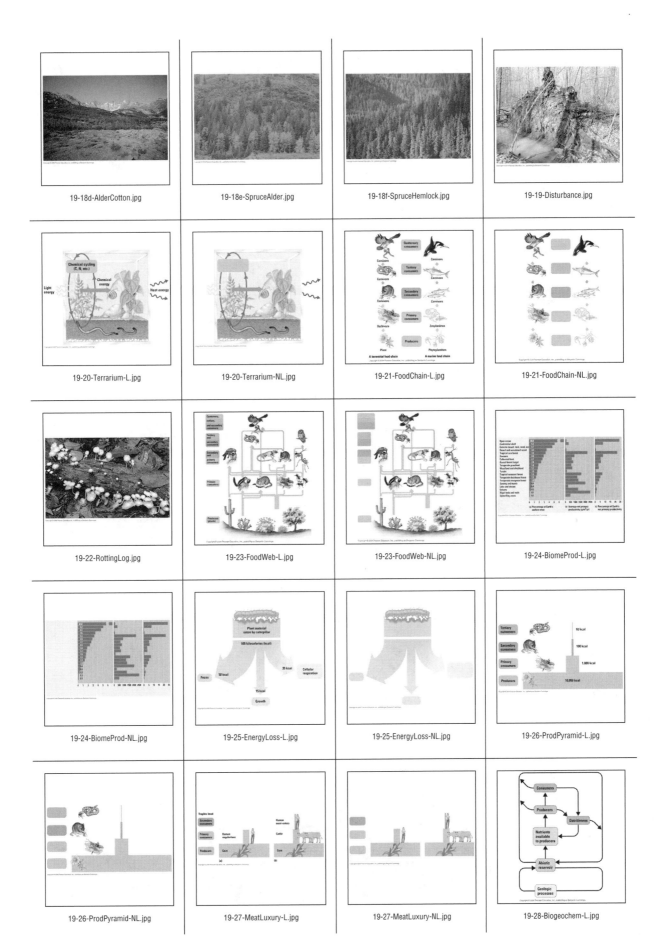

19-18d-AlderCotton.jpg

19-18e-SpruceAlder.jpg

19-18f-SpruceHemlock.jpg

19-19-Disturbance.jpg

19-20-Terrarium-L.jpg

19-20-Terrarium-NL.jpg

19-21-FoodChain-L.jpg

19-21-FoodChain-NL.jpg

19-22-RottingLog.jpg

19-23-FoodWeb-L.jpg

19-23-FoodWeb-NL.jpg

19-24-BiomeProd-L.jpg

19-24-BiomeProd-NL.jpg

19-25-EnergyLoss-L.jpg

19-25-EnergyLoss-NL.jpg

19-26-ProdPyramid-L.jpg

19-26-ProdPyramid-NL.jpg

19-27-MeatLuxury-L.jpg

19-27-MeatLuxury-NL.jpg

19-28-Biogeochem-L.jpg

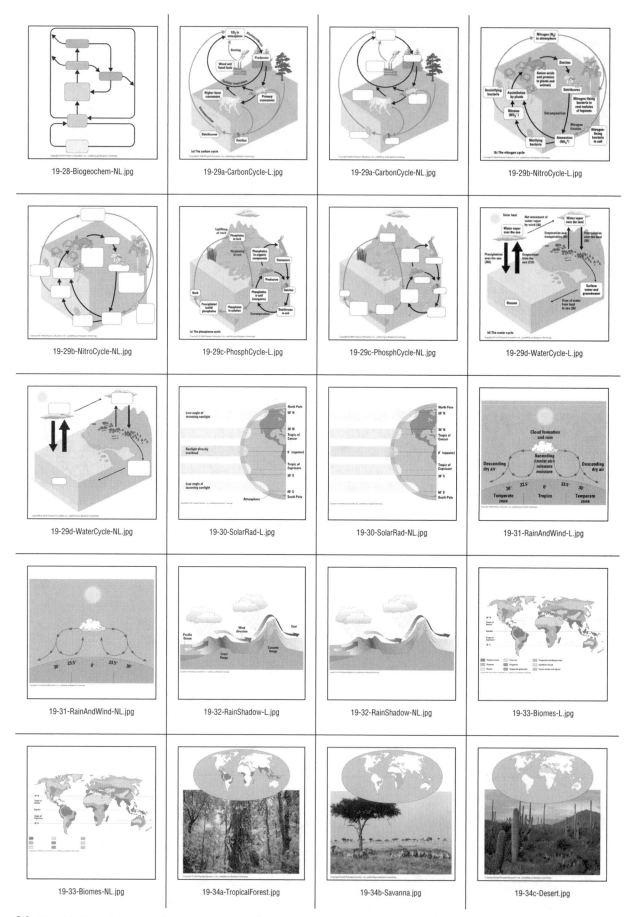

19-28-Biogeochem-NL.jpg

19-29a-CarbonCycle-L.jpg

19-29a-CarbonCycle-NL.jpg

19-29b-NitroCycle-L.jpg

19-29b-NitroCycle-NL.jpg

19-29c-PhosphCycle-L.jpg

19-29c-PhosphCycle-NL.jpg

19-29d-WaterCycle-L.jpg

19-29d-WaterCycle-NL.jpg

19-30-SolarRad-L.jpg

19-30-SolarRad-NL.jpg

19-31-RainAndWind-L.jpg

19-31-RainAndWind-NL.jpg

19-32-RainShadow-L.jpg

19-32-RainShadow-NL.jpg

19-33-Biomes-L.jpg

19-33-Biomes-NL.jpg

19-34a-TropicalForest.jpg

19-34b-Savanna.jpg

19-34c-Desert.jpg

19-34d-Chaparral.jpg

19-34e-Grassland.jpg

19-34f-Deciduous.jpg

19-34g-Coniferous.jpg

19-34h-Tundra.jpg

19-35a-GreatLakes.jpg

19-35b-Stream.jpg

19-35c-Wetland.jpg

19-36-RiverBasin-L.jpg

19-36-RiverBasin-NL.jpg

19-37-Estuary.jpg

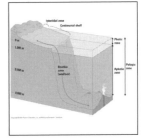
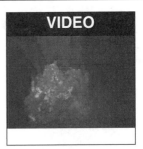

19-38-OceanZones-L.jpg

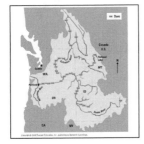

19-38-OceanZones-NL.jpg

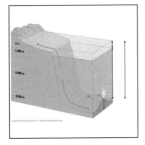

19-39-TidePool.jpg

VIDEO

19-40-HydtherVideo-B.mov

VIDEO

19-40-HydtherVideo-S.mov

VIDEO

19-40-TubewrmVideo-B.mov

VIDEO

19-40-TubewrmVideo-S.mov

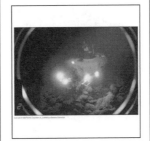

19-40a-Alvin.jpg

19-40b-UnderseaVent.jpg

19-41-Coevolution-L.jpg

19-41-Coevolution-NL.jpg

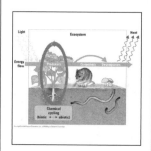

19-SK01-ChemCyc-L.jpg

19-SK01-ChemCyc-NL.jpg

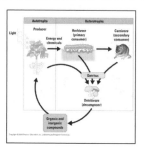

19-SK02-FoodChain-L.jpg

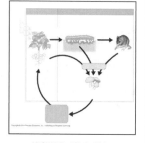

19-SK02-FoodChain-NL.jpg

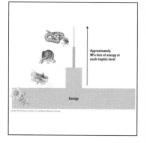

19-SK03-EnergyPyr-L.jpg

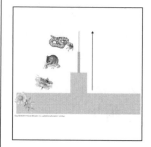

19-SK03-EnergyPyr-NL.jpg

20-00a-HumEdges.jpg

20-00b-RainForest.jpg

20-00c-Eagle.jpg

20-00d-Starlings.jpg

20-01a-Snakehead.jpg

20-01b-Caulerpa.jpg

20-02-OpenPitMine.jpg

20-03a-Kudzu.jpg

20-03b-Starlings.jpg

20-03c-ArgentineAnts.jpg

20-03d-ZebraMussels.jpg

20-04-CO2Producers.jpg

20-05-Deforestation.jpg

20-06a-DammedHubbard.jpg

20-06b-LoggedHubbard.jpg

20-06c-NitrateLos-L.jpg

20-06c-NitrateLos-NL.jpg

20-07-Biomagnific-L.jpg

20-07-Biomagnific-NL.jpg

20-08-Earthrise.jpg

20-09-CO2Conc.jpg

20-10-Greenhouse-L.jpg

20-10-Greenhouse-NL.jpg

20-11-GlobalWarm-L.jpg

20-11-GlobalWarm-NL.jpg

20-12ab-Ozone-L.jpg

20-12ab-Ozone-NL.jpg

20-12c-SunLovers.jpg

20-13-CoralReef.jpg

20-14a-Eagle.jpg

20-14b-RiverDolphin.jpg

20-14c-JavanRhino.jpg

20-15a-Clearcutting.jpg

20-15b-NilePerch.jpg

20-15c-BluefinTuna.jpg

20-16-RosyPeriwinkle.jpg

20-17a-Chaparral.jpg

20-17b-TroplForst.jpg

20-17c-HotSpots-L.jpg

20-17c-HotSpots-NL.jpg

20-17c-TropicalFor.jpg

20-18a-Fragmentation.jpg

20-18b-SpottedOwl.jpg

20-19a-RedCockaded.jpg

20-19b-Woodpecker.jpg

20-19c-NoWoodpecker.jpg

20-20a-NaturalEdges.jpg

20-20b-HumEdges.jpg

20-21-HumCorridor.jpg

20-22a-ZonedRes-L.jpg

20-22a-ZonedRes-NL.jpg

20-22b-CostaRica.jpg

20-23-EOwilson.jpg

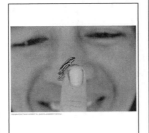

20-24-Biophilia.jpg

20-SK01-DDTEagle-L.jpg

20-SK01-DDTEagle-NL.jpg

20-SK02-BioLevel-L.jpg

20-SK02-BioLevel-NL.jpg

20-SK03-BioCrisis-L.jpg

20-SK03-BioCrisis-NL.jpg

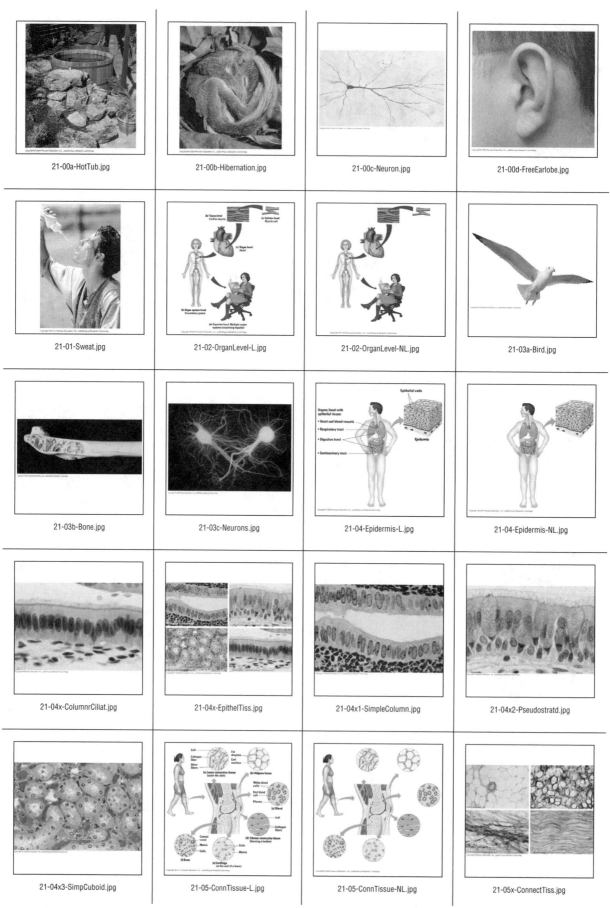

21-00a-HotTub.jpg

21-00b-Hibernation.jpg

21-00c-Neuron.jpg

21-00d-FreeEarlobe.jpg

21-01-Sweat.jpg

21-02-OrganLevel-L.jpg

21-02-OrganLevel-NL.jpg

21-03a-Bird.jpg

21-03b-Bone.jpg

21-03c-Neurons.jpg

21-04-Epidermis-L.jpg

21-04-Epidermis-NL.jpg

21-04x-ColumnrCiliat.jpg

21-04x-EpithelTiss.jpg

21-04x1-SimpleColumn.jpg

21-04x2-Pseudostratd.jpg

21-04x3-SimpCuboid.jpg

21-05-ConnTissue-L.jpg

21-05-ConnTissue-NL.jpg

21-05x-ConnectTiss.jpg

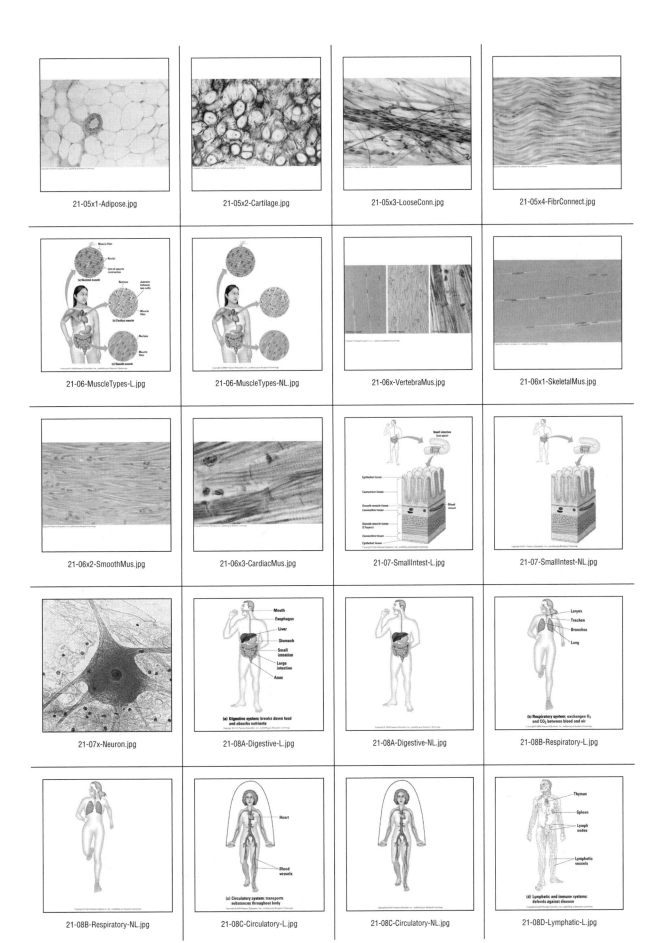

21-05x1-Adipose.jpg

21-05x2-Cartilage.jpg

21-05x3-LooseConn.jpg

21-05x4-FibrConnect.jpg

21-06-MuscleTypes-L.jpg

21-06-MuscleTypes-NL.jpg

21-06x-VertebraMus.jpg

21-06x1-SkeletalMus.jpg

21-06x2-SmoothMus.jpg

21-06x3-CardiacMus.jpg

21-07-SmallIntest-L.jpg

21-07-SmallIntest-NL.jpg

21-07x-Neuron.jpg

21-08A-Digestive-L.jpg

21-08A-Digestive-NL.jpg

21-08B-Respiratory-L.jpg

21-08B-Respiratory-NL.jpg

21-08C-Circulatory-L.jpg

21-08C-Circulatory-NL.jpg

21-08D-Lymphatic-L.jpg

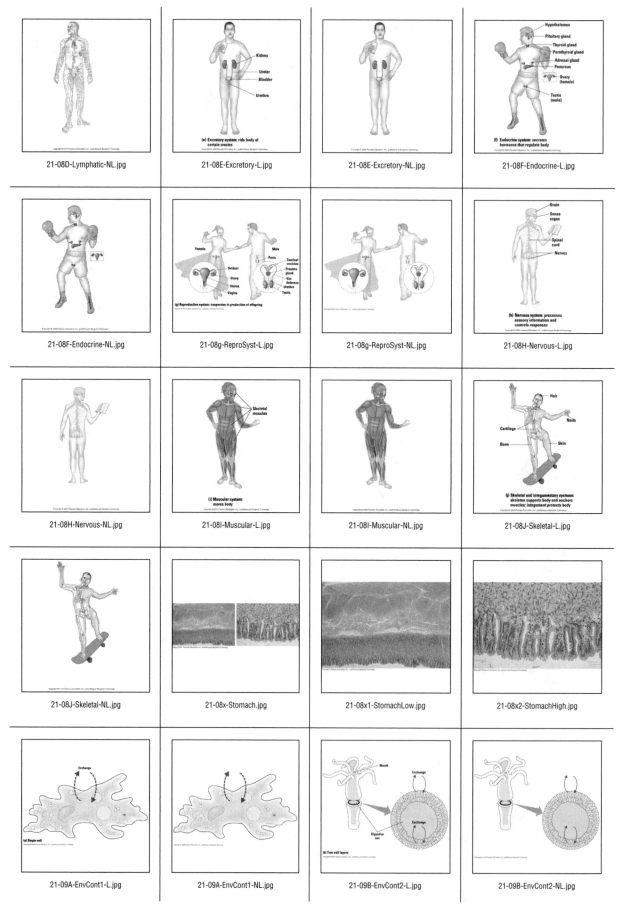

21-08D-Lymphatic-NL.jpg

21-08E-Excretory-L.jpg

21-08E-Excretory-NL.jpg

21-08F-Endocrine-L.jpg

21-08F-Endocrine-NL.jpg

21-08g-ReproSyst-L.jpg

21-08g-ReproSyst-NL.jpg

21-08H-Nervous-L.jpg

21-08H-Nervous-NL.jpg

21-08I-Muscular-L.jpg

21-08I-Muscular-NL.jpg

21-08J-Skeletal-L.jpg

21-08J-Skeletal-NL.jpg

21-08x-Stomach.jpg

21-08x1-StomachLow.jpg

21-08x2-StomachHigh.jpg

21-09A-EnvCont1-L.jpg

21-09A-EnvCont1-NL.jpg

21-09B-EnvCont2-L.jpg

21-09B-EnvCont2-NL.jpg

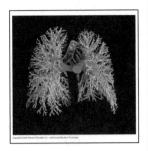

21-10-Lungs.jpg

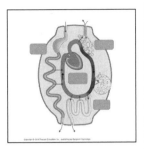

21-11-ExtEnIntEnv-L.jpg

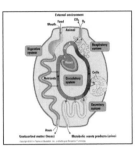

21-11-ExtEnIntEnv-NL.jpg

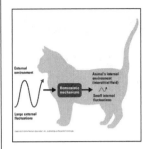

21-12-Homeostatic-L.jpg

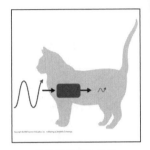

21-12-Homeostatic-NL.jpg

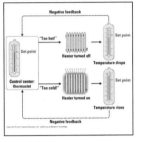

21-13-Thermostat-L.jpg

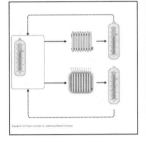

21-13-Thermostat-NL.jpg

21-14a-Thermoreg.jpg

21-14b-ShaqSweat.jpg

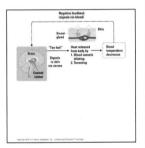

21-15-L1-NegFeed-L.jpg

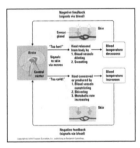

21-15-L2-FeedLoop-L.jpg

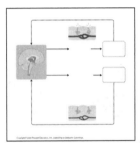

21-15-L2-FeedLoop-NL.jpg

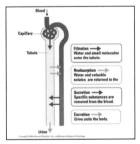

21-16-KidneyFxn-L.jpg

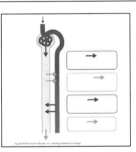

21-16-KidneyFxn-NL.jpg

21-17-BowCapsulAnim.mov

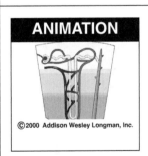

21-17-CollDuctAnim.mov

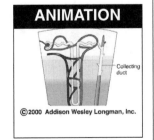

21-17-EffectADHAnim.mov

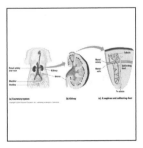

21-17-Kidney-L.jpg

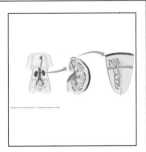

21-17-Kidney-NL.jpg

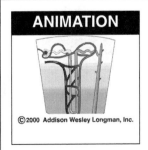

21-17-LoopHenleAnim.mov

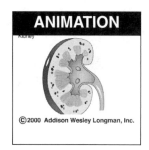

21-17-NephrIntrAnim.mov

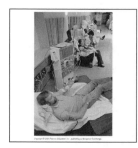

21-18a-DialysisPat.jpg

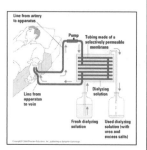

21-18b-Dialysis-L.jpg

21-18b-Dialysis-NL.jpg

21-19a-Dolphins.jpg

21-19b-Seal.jpg

21-19c-Shark.jpg

21-19d-Tuna.jpg

21-19e-Penguins.jpg

21-19f-Submarine.jpg

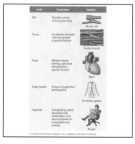

21-SK01-AnimalOrg.jpg

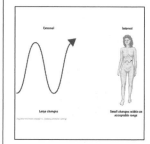

21-SK02-Homeosts-L.jpg

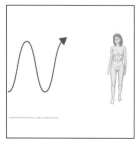

21-SK02-Homeosts-NL.jpg

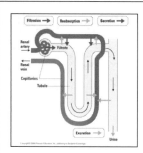

21-SK03-Kidneys-L.jpg

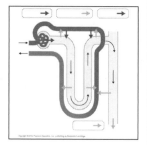

21-SK03-Kidneys-NL.jpg

Chapter 22 Nutrition and Digestion

22-00a-Hamburger.jpg

22-00b-Hpylori.jpg

22-00c-Saliva.jpg

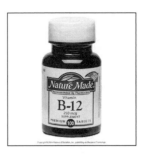

22-00d-B12Supple.jpg

22-01-Sigler.jpg

22-02-ShkSealVideo-B.mov

22-02-ShkSealVideo-S.mov

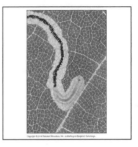

22-02a-Herbivore.jpg

22-02b-Carnivore.jpg

22-02c-Omnivore.jpg

22-02x-AnimEatingCol.jpg

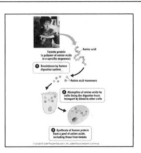

22-03-Proteins-L.jpg

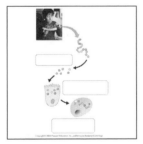

22-03-Proteins-NL.jpg

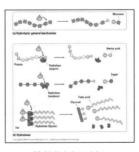

22-04-Hydrolases-L.jpg

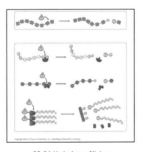

22-04-Hydrolases-NL.jpg

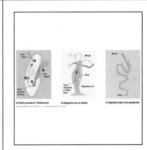

22-05-GItracts-L.jpg

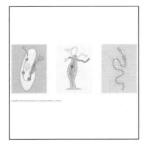

22-05-GItracts-NL.jpg

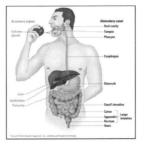

22-06-HumGItract-L.jpg

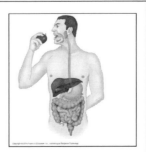

22-06-HumGItract-NL.jpg

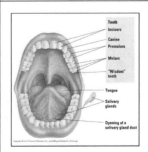

22-07-Mouth-L.jpg

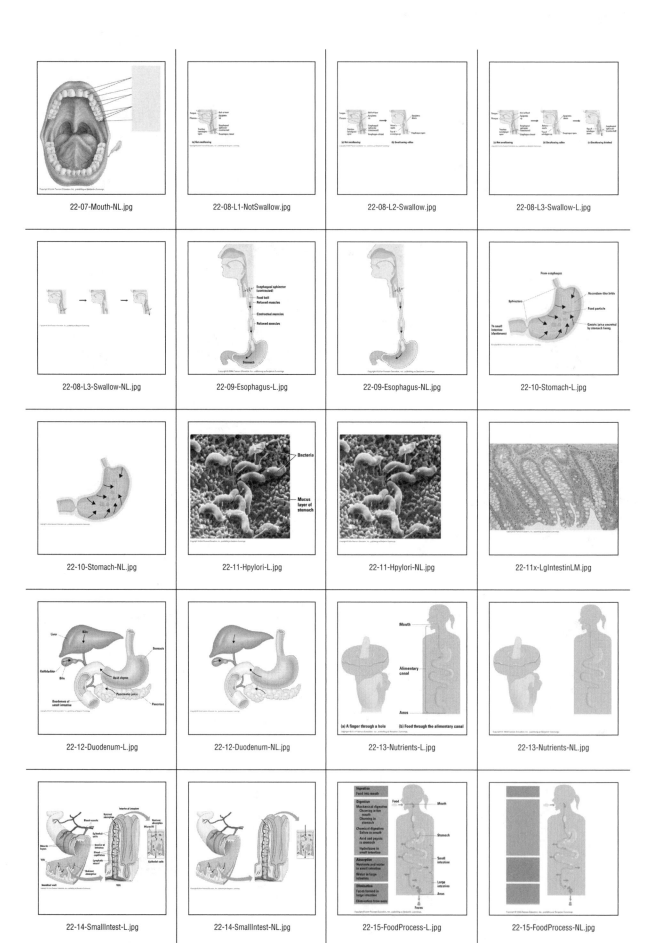

22-07-Mouth-NL.jpg

22-08-L1-NotSwallow.jpg

22-08-L2-Swallow.jpg

22-08-L3-Swallow-L.jpg

22-08-L3-Swallow-NL.jpg

22-09-Esophagus-L.jpg

22-09-Esophagus-NL.jpg

22-10-Stomach-L.jpg

22-10-Stomach-NL.jpg

22-11-Hpylori-L.jpg

22-11-Hpylori-NL.jpg

22-11x-LgIntestinLM.jpg

22-12-Duodenum-L.jpg

22-12-Duodenum-NL.jpg

22-13-Nutrients-L.jpg

22-13-Nutrients-NL.jpg

22-14-SmallIntest-L.jpg

22-14-SmallIntest-NL.jpg

22-15-FoodProcess-L.jpg

22-15-FoodProcess-NL.jpg

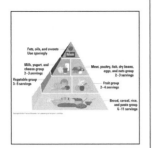

22-16-FoodPyramid-L.jpg

22-16-FoodPyramid-NL.jpg

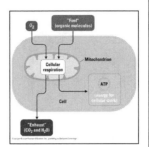

22-17-CellResp-L.jpg

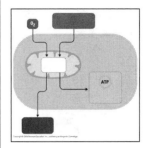

22-17-CellResp-NL.jpg

22-18a-EssenAAs-L.jpg

22-18a-EssenAAs-NL.jpg

22-18b-CombProteins.jpg

22-19-NutritionLabel.jpg

22-20-Kwashiorkor.jpg

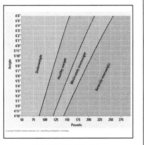

22-21-HealthyWgt-L.jpg

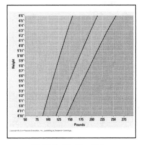

22-21-HealthyWgt-NL.jpg

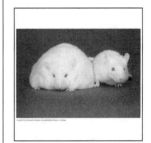

22-22-HungryMouse.jpg

22-23-BadFoodChoices.jpg

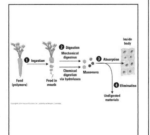

22-SK01-FdProcess-L.jpg

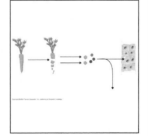

22-SK01-FdProcess-NL.jpg

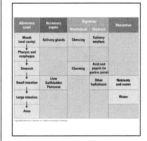

22-SK02-DigestMap.jpg

22-T01-KcalExer.jpg

22-T02-Vitamins.jpg

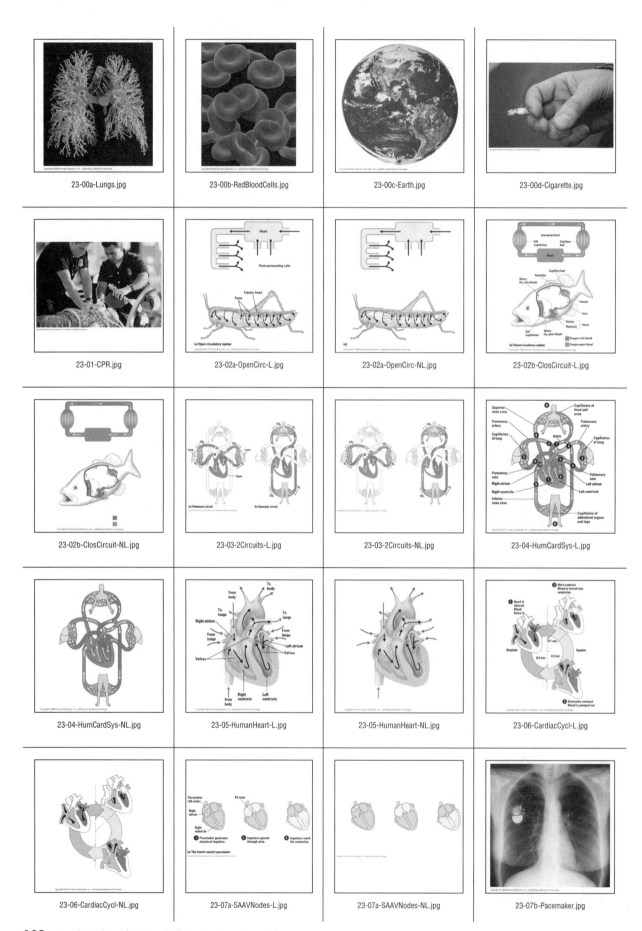

23-00a-Lungs.jpg

23-00b-RedBloodCells.jpg

23-00c-Earth.jpg

23-00d-Cigarette.jpg

23-01-CPR.jpg

23-02a-OpenCirc-L.jpg

23-02a-OpenCirc-NL.jpg

23-02b-ClosCircuit-L.jpg

23-02b-ClosCircuit-NL.jpg

23-03-2Circuits-L.jpg

23-03-2Circuits-NL.jpg

23-04-HumCardSys-L.jpg

23-04-HumCardSys-NL.jpg

23-05-HumanHeart-L.jpg

23-05-HumanHeart-NL.jpg

23-06-CardiacCycl-L.jpg

23-06-CardiacCycl-NL.jpg

23-07a-SAAVNodes-L.jpg

23-07a-SAAVNodes-NL.jpg

23-07b-Pacemaker.jpg

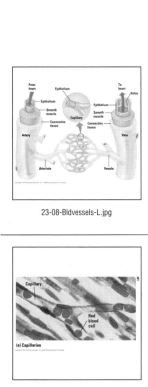

23-08-Bldvessels-L.jpg

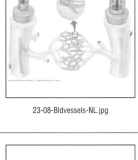

23-08-Bldvessels-NL.jpg

23-09-Capillary-L.jpg

23-09-Capillary-NL.jpg

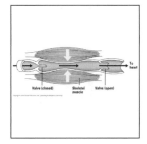

23-09a-Capillary-L.jpg

23-09a-Capillary-NL.jpg

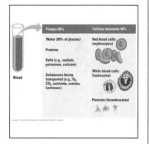

23-09B-Vein-L.jpg

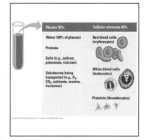

23-09B-Vein-NL.jpg

23-10-VenousFlow-L.jpg

23-10-VenousFlow-NL.jpg

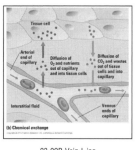

23-11-BloodComp-L.jpg

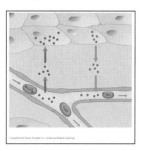

23-11-BloodComp-NL.jpg

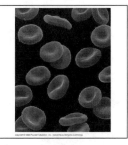

23-12-RedBloodCells.jpg

23-13-BloodClot-L.jpg

23-13-BloodClot-NL.jpg

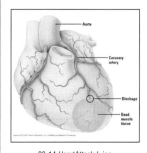

23-14-HeartAttack-L.jpg

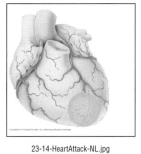

23-14-HeartAttack-NL.jpg

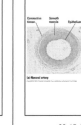

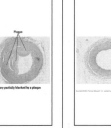

23-15-Arteries-L.jpg

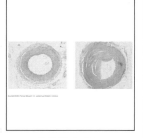

23-15-Arteries-NL.jpg

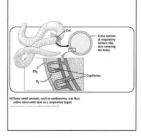

23-16a-Earthworm-L.jpg

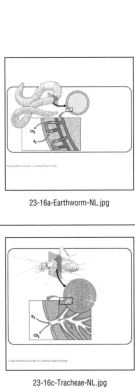

23-16a-Earthworm-NL.jpg

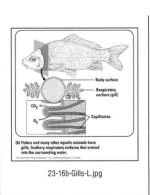

23-16b-Gills-L.jpg

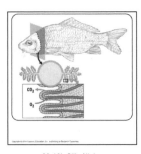

23-16b-Gills-NL.jpg

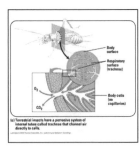

23-16c-Tracheae-L.jpg

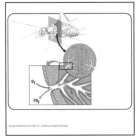

23-16c-Tracheae-NL.jpg

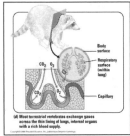

23-16d-Lungs-L.jpg

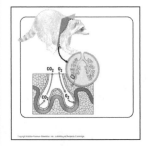

23-16d-Lungs-NL.jpg

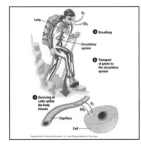

23-17-GasExchange-L.jpg

23-17-GasExchange-NL.jpg

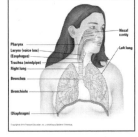

23-18-HumRespSyst-L.jpg

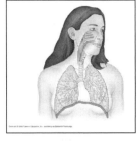

23-18-HumRespSyst-NL.jpg

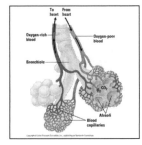

23-19-Alveoli-L.jpg

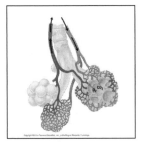

23-19-Alveoli-NL.jpg

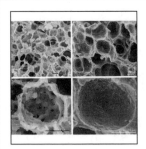

23-19x1-AlveoliSEMs.jpg

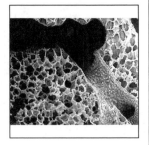

23-19x2-AlveoliSEM.jpg

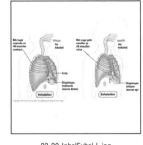

23-20-InhalExhal-L.jpg

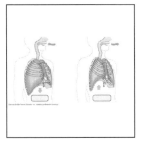

23-20-InhalExhal-NL.jpg

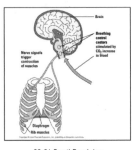

23-21-BreathReg-L.jpg

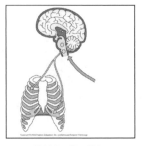

23-21-BreathReg-NL.jpg

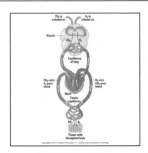

23-22-GasTrnsport-L.jpg

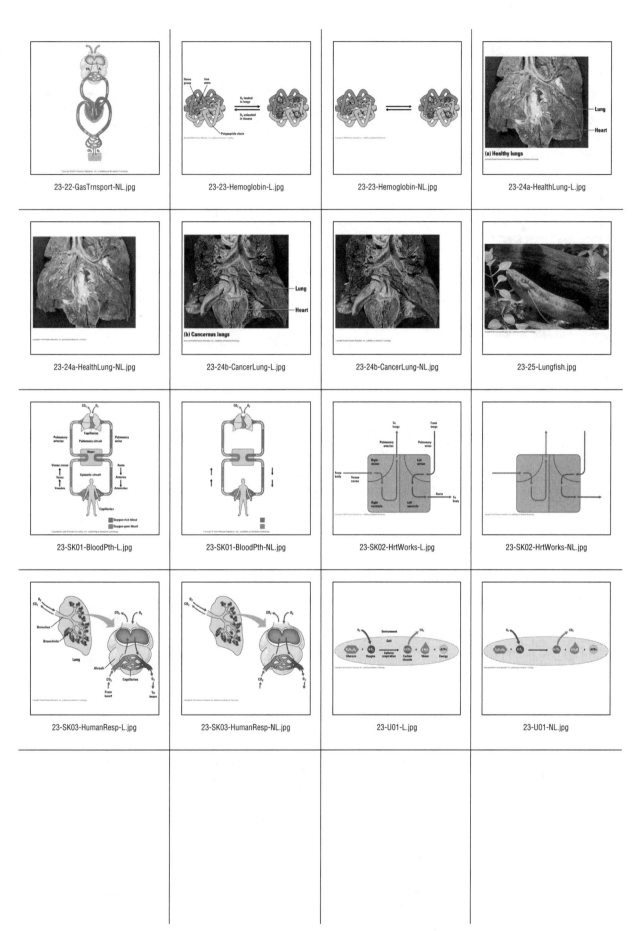

23-22-GasTrnsport-NL.jpg

23-23-Hemoglobin-L.jpg

23-23-Hemoglobin-NL.jpg

23-24a-HealthLung-L.jpg

23-24a-HealthLung-NL.jpg

23-24b-CancerLung-L.jpg

23-24b-CancerLung-NL.jpg

23-25-Lungfish.jpg

23-SK01-BloodPth-L.jpg

23-SK01-BloodPth-NL.jpg

23-SK02-HrtWorks-L.jpg

23-SK02-HrtWorks-NL.jpg

23-SK03-HumanResp-L.jpg

23-SK03-HumanResp-NL.jpg

23-U01-L.jpg

23-U01-NL.jpg

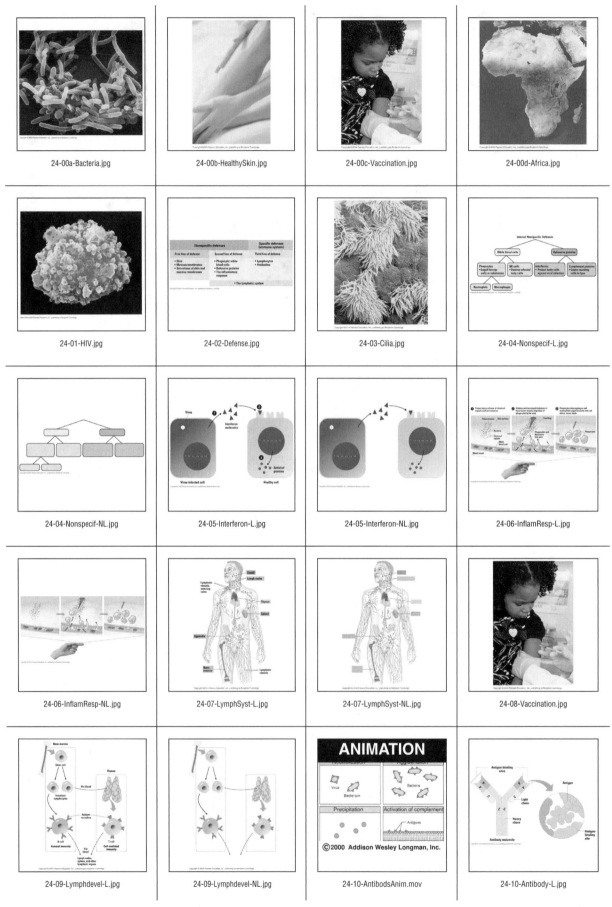

24-00a-Bacteria.jpg

24-00b-HealthySkin.jpg

24-00c-Vaccination.jpg

24-00d-Africa.jpg

24-01-HIV.jpg

24-02-Defense.jpg

24-03-Cilia.jpg

24-04-Nonspecif-L.jpg

24-04-Nonspecif-NL.jpg

24-05-Interferon-L.jpg

24-05-Interferon-NL.jpg

24-06-InflamResp-L.jpg

24-06-InflamResp-NL.jpg

24-07-LymphSyst-L.jpg

24-07-LymphSyst-NL.jpg

24-08-Vaccination.jpg

24-09-Lymphdevel-L.jpg

24-09-Lymphdevel-NL.jpg

24-10-AntibodsAnim.mov

24-10-Antibody-L.jpg

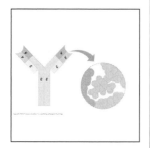

24-10-Antibody-NL.jpg

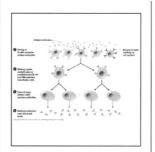

24-11-ClonalSelec-L.jpg

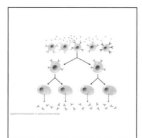

24-11-ClonalSelec-NL.jpg

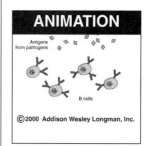

24-11-RoleBCellAnim.mov

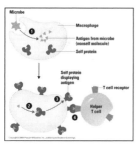

24-12-HelperTMacr-L.jpg

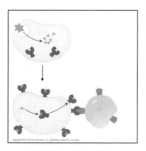

24-12-HelperTMacr-NL.jpg

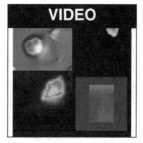

24-12-TCellRcVideo-S.mov

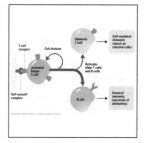

24-13-HelperT-L.jpg

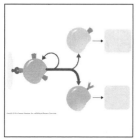

24-13-HelperT-NL.jpg

24-13-HelpTCellAnim.mov

24-14-CytotoxicT-L.jpg

24-14-CytotoxicT-NL.jpg

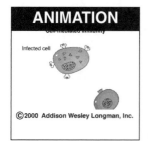

24-14-CytoxTCellAnim.mov

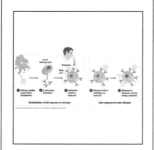

24-15-Allergies-L.jpg

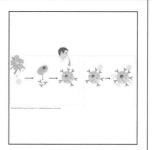

24-15-Allergies-NL.jpg

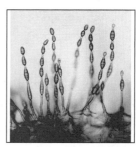

24-15x-AllergySpores.jpg

24-16-Epinephrine.jpg

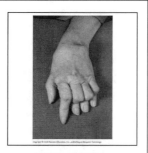

24-17-RheumatdArth.jpg

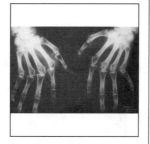

24-17x-ArthritisXray.jpg

24-18-AIDSeducation.jpg

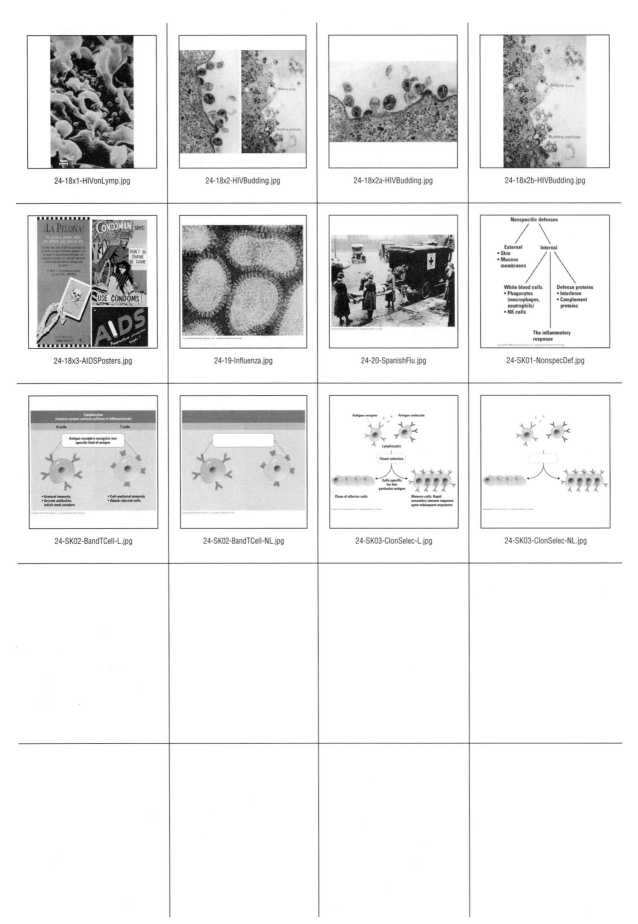

24-18x1-HIVonLymp.jpg

24-18x2-HIVBudding.jpg

24-18x2a-HIVBudding.jpg

24-18x2b-HIVBudding.jpg

24-18x3-AIDSPosters.jpg

24-19-Influenza.jpg

24-20-SpanishFlu.jpg

24-SK01-NonspecDef.jpg

24-SK02-BandTCell-L.jpg

24-SK02-BandTCell-NL.jpg

24-SK03-ClonSelec-L.jpg

24-SK03-ClonSelec-NL.jpg

Chapter 25 Hormones

25-00a-Stress.jpg

25-00b-Dwarfism.jpg

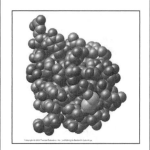

25-00c-Hormones.jpg

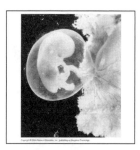

25-00d-HumEmbryo.jpg

25-01-HormAndAging.jpg

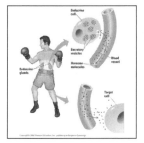

25-02-Secretion-L.jpg

25-02-Secretion-NL.jpg

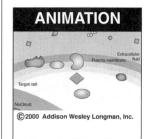

25-03-NonstrHormAnim.mov

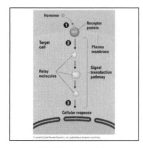

25-03-SignalTrans-L.jpg

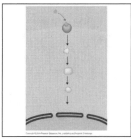

25-03-SignalTrans-NL.jpg

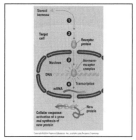

25-04-Intracell-L.jpg

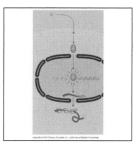

25-04-Intracell-NL.jpg

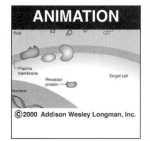

25-04-SterodHormAnim.mov

25-05-GlandsLoc-L.jpg

25-05-GlandsLoc-NL.jpg

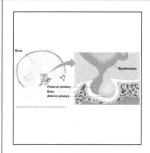

25-06-Pituitary-L.jpg

25-06-Pituitary-NL.jpg

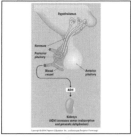

25-07-ADH-L.jpg

25-07-ADH-NL.jpg

25-08a-Gigantism.jpg

25-08b-Acromegaly.jpg

25-08c-Dwarfism.jpg

25-09-Goiter.jpg

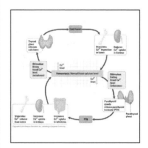

25-10-CalciumHom-L.jpg

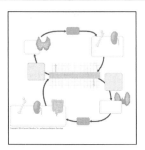

25-10-CalciumHom-NL.jpg

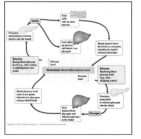

25-11-GlucoseHom-L.jpg

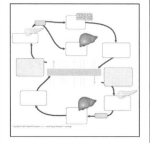

25-11-GlucoseHom-NL.jpg

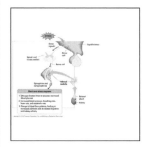

25-12-L1-ShortStress.jpg

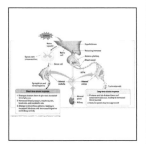

25-12-L2-Stress-L.jpg

25-12-L2-Stress-NL.jpg

25-13-PRLposFeedbck.jpg

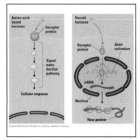

25-SK01-HormResp-L.jpg

25-SK01-HormResp-NL.jpg

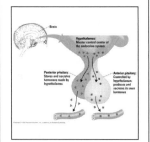

25-SK02-Endocrne-L.jpg

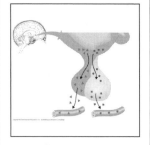

25-SK02-Endocrne-NL.jpg

25-T01a-EndocGlands.jpg

25-T01b-EndocGlands.jpg

Chapter 26 Reproduction and Development

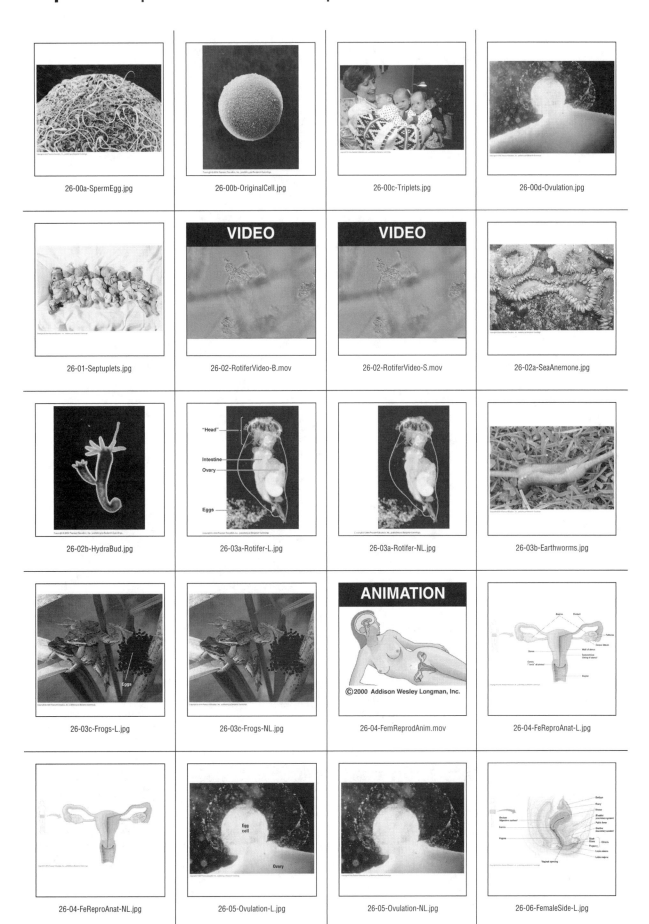

26-00a-SpermEgg.jpg

26-00b-OriginalCell.jpg

26-00c-Triplets.jpg

26-00d-Ovulation.jpg

26-01-Septuplets.jpg

26-02-RotiferVideo-B.mov

26-02-RotiferVideo-S.mov

26-02a-SeaAnemone.jpg

26-02b-HydraBud.jpg

26-03a-Rotifer-L.jpg

26-03a-Rotifer-NL.jpg

26-03b-Earthworms.jpg

26-03c-Frogs-L.jpg

26-03c-Frogs-NL.jpg

26-04-FemReprodAnim.mov

26-04-FeReproAnat-L.jpg

26-04-FeReproAnat-NL.jpg

26-05-Ovulation-L.jpg

26-05-Ovulation-NL.jpg

26-06-FemaleSide-L.jpg

26-06-FemaleSide-NL.jpg

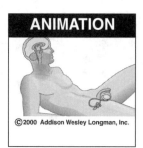

26-07-MaleHormAnim.mov

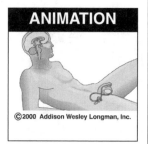

26-07-MaleReprodAnim.mov

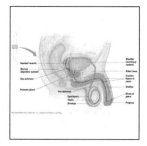

26-07a-MaleSide-L.jpg

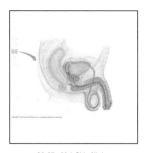

26-07a-MaleSide-NL.jpg

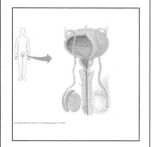

26-07b-MaleFront-NL.jpg

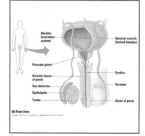

26-07b-MaleRepro-L.jpg

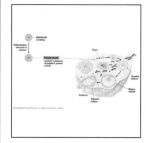

26-08-L1-1Oocyte.jpg

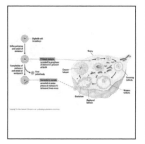

26-08-L2-2Oocyte.jpg

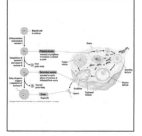

26-08-L3-Oogen-L.jpg

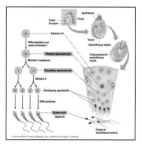

26-08-L3-Oogen-NL.jpg

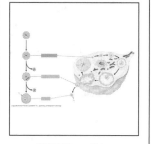

26-09-SpermProd-L.jpg

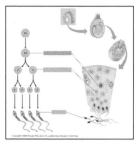

26-09-SpermProd-NL.jpg

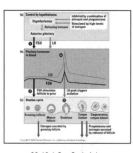

26-10-1-OvarCycle-L.jpg

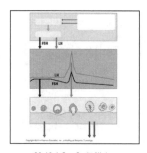

26-10-1-OvarCycle-NL.jpg

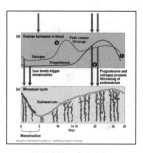

26-10-2-MenstCycle-L.jpg

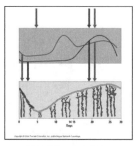

26-10-2-MenstCycle-NL.jpg

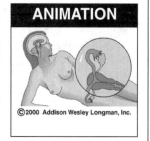

26-10-OvulationAnim.mov

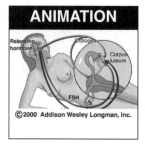

26-10-PostOvulaAnim.mov

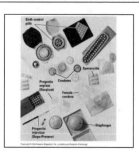

26-11-BirthContr-L.jpg

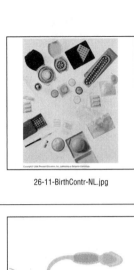
26-11-BirthContr-NL.jpg

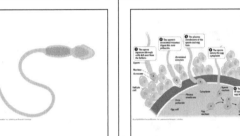
26-12-InVitro.jpg

26-13-SpermEgg.jpg

26-14-Sperm-L.jpg

26-14-Sperm-NL.jpg

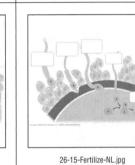
26-15-Fertilize-L.jpg

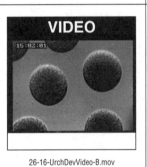
26-15-Fertilize-NL.jpg

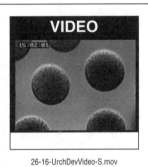
26-16-EmbryoDev-L.jpg

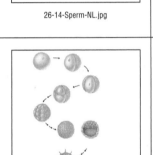
26-16-EmbryoDev-NL.jpg

VIDEO
26-16-FrogDevVideo-S.mov

VIDEO
15:02:01
26-16-UrchDevVideo-B.mov

VIDEO
15:02:01
26-16-UrchDevVideo-S.mov

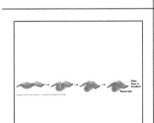
26-17-NeuralTube-L.jpg

26-17-NeuralTube-NL.jpg

26-18-EyeDevel-L.jpg

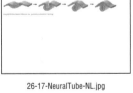
26-18-EyeDevel-NL.jpg

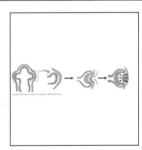
26-19-Early Stages-NL.jpg

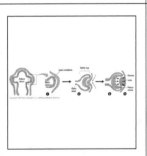
26-19-EarlyStages-L.jpg

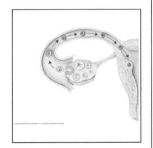
26-20-Blastocyst-L.jpg

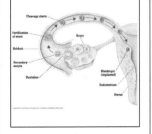
26-20-Blastocyst-NL.jpg

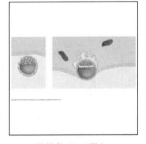
26-20-Blastocyst-NL.jpg

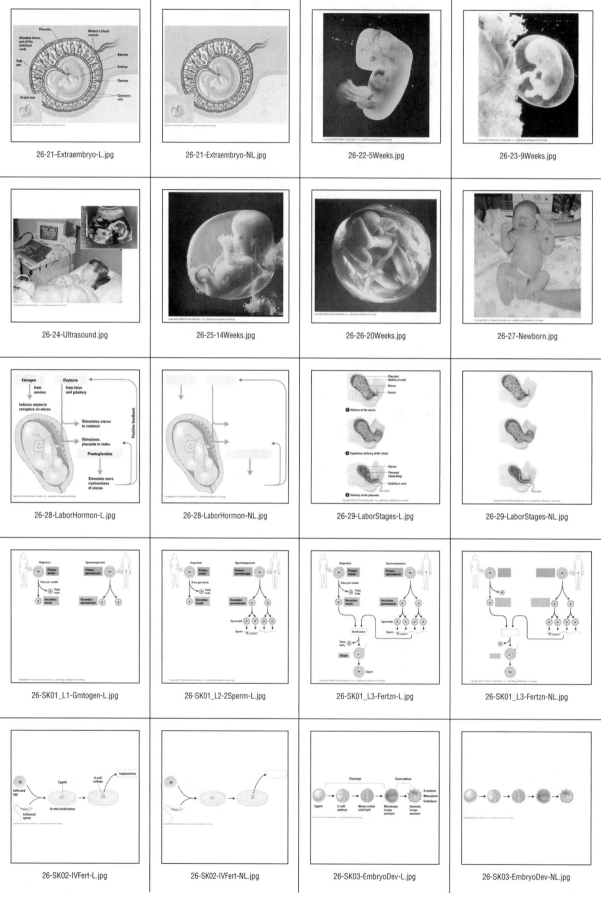

26-21-Extraembryo-L.jpg

26-21-Extraembryo-NL.jpg

26-22-5Weeks.jpg

26-23-9Weeks.jpg

26-24-Ultrasound.jpg

26-25-14Weeks.jpg

26-26-20Weeks.jpg

26-27-Newborn.jpg

26-28-LaborHormon-L.jpg

26-28-LaborHormon-NL.jpg

26-29-LaborStages-L.jpg

26-29-LaborStages-NL.jpg

26-SK01_L1-Gmtogen-L.jpg

26-SK01_L2-2Sperm-L.jpg

26-SK01_L3-Fertzn-L.jpg

26-SK01_L3-Fertzn-NL.jpg

26-SK02-IVFert-L.jpg

26-SK02-IVFert-NL.jpg

26-SK03-EmbryoDev-L.jpg

26-SK03-EmbryoDev-NL.jpg

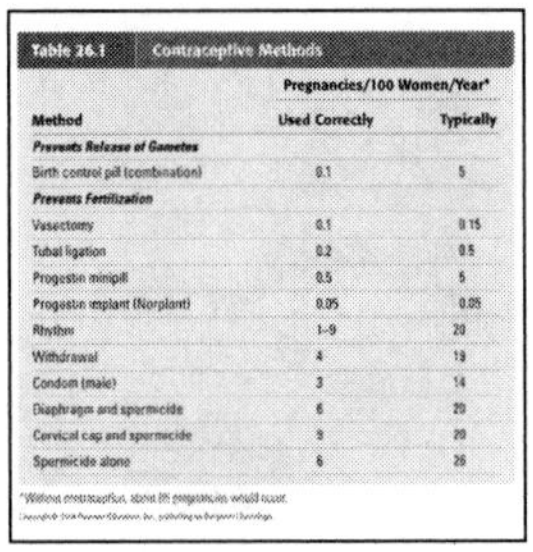

Table 26.1 Contraceptive Methods	Pregnancies/100 Women/Year*	
Method	Used Correctly	Typically
Prevents Release of Gametes		
Birth control pill (combination)	0.1	5
Prevents Fertilization		
Vasectomy	0.1	0.15
Tubal ligation	0.2	0.5
Progestin minipill	0.5	5
Progestin implant (Norplant)	0.05	0.05
Rhythm	1–9	20
Withdrawal	4	19
Condom (male)	3	14
Diaphragm and spermicide	6	20
Cervical cap and spermicide	9	20
Spermicide alone	6	26

*Without contraception, about 85 pregnancies would occur.

26-T01-Contraception.jpg

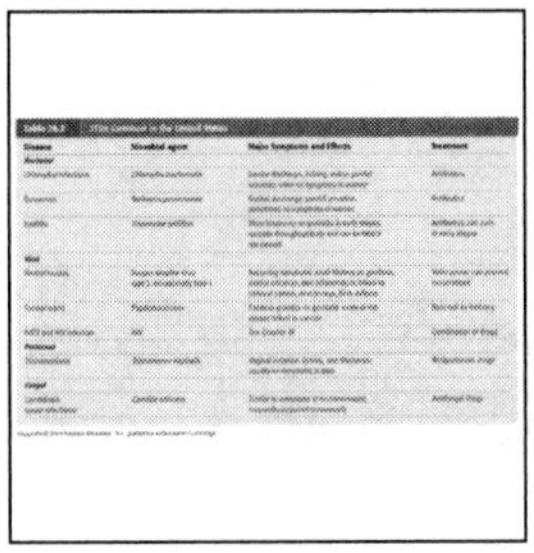

26-T02-STDs.jpg

27-00a-BulletTrain.jpg

27-00b-Antidepress.jpg

27-00c-Greyscale.jpg

27-00d-HalfBrain.jpg

27-01-Depression.jpg

27-02-L1-SensInput.jpg

27-02-L2-Integration.jpg

27-02-L3-NerSyFxn-L.jpg

27-02-L3-NerSyFxn-NL.jpg

27-03-Neuron-L.jpg

27-03-Neuron-NL.jpg

27-03A-Npathway-L.jpg

27-03A-NPathway-NL.jpg

27-03B-NCell-L.jpg

27-03B-NCell-NL.jpg

27-04-ActnPotentAnim.mov

27-04-ActPotent-L.jpg

27-04-ActPotent-NL.jpg

27-04-RestPotentAnim.mov

27-05-PropActPot-L.jpg

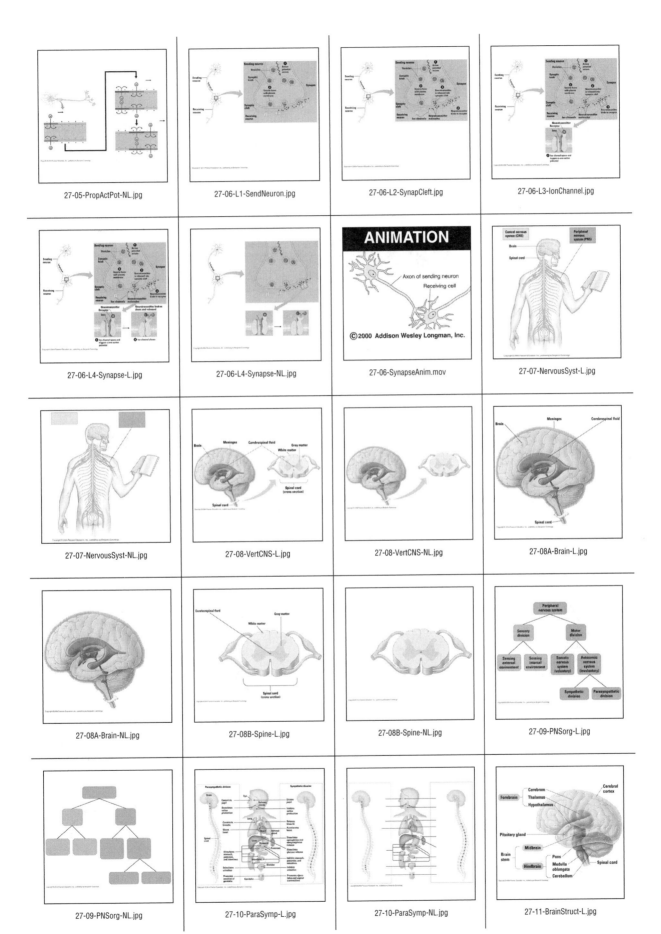

27-05-PropActPot-NL.jpg

27-06-L1-SendNeuron.jpg

27-06-L2-SynapCleft.jpg

27-06-L3-IonChannel.jpg

27-06-L4-Synapse-L.jpg

27-06-L4-Synapse-NL.jpg

27-06-SynapseAnim.mov

27-07-NervousSyst-L.jpg

27-07-NervousSyst-NL.jpg

27-08-VertCNS-L.jpg

27-08-VertCNS-NL.jpg

27-08A-Brain-L.jpg

27-08A-Brain-NL.jpg

27-08B-Spine-L.jpg

27-08B-Spine-NL.jpg

27-09-PNSorg-L.jpg

27-09-PNSorg-NL.jpg

27-10-ParaSymp-L.jpg

27-10-ParaSymp-NL.jpg

27-11-BrainStruct-L.jpg

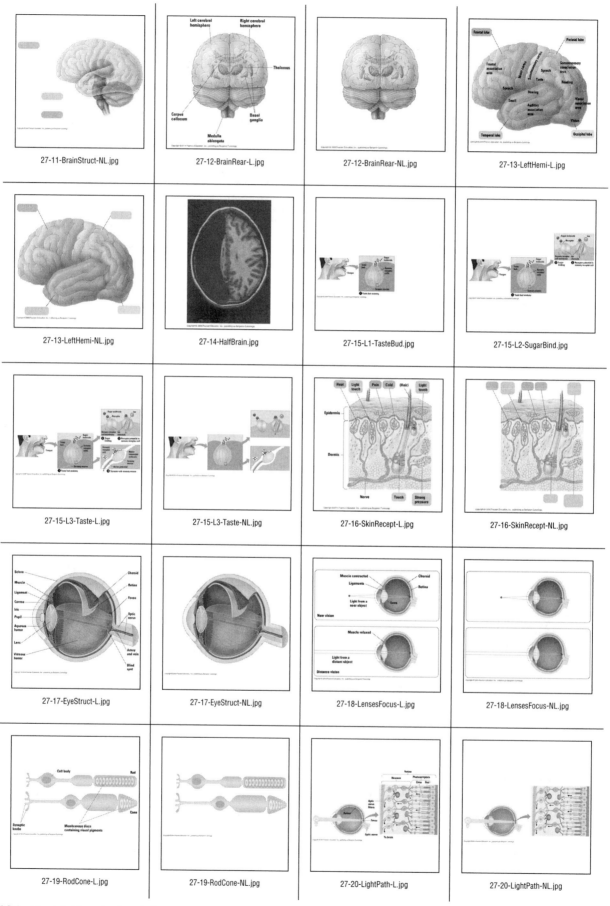

27-11-BrainStruct-NL.jpg

27-12-BrainRear-L.jpg

27-12-BrainRear-NL.jpg

27-13-LeftHemi-L.jpg

27-13-LeftHemi-NL.jpg

27-14-HalfBrain.jpg

27-15-L1-TasteBud.jpg

27-15-L2-SugarBind.jpg

27-15-L3-Taste-L.jpg

27-15-L3-Taste-NL.jpg

27-16-SkinRecept-L.jpg

27-16-SkinRecept-NL.jpg

27-17-EyeStruct-L.jpg

27-17-EyeStruct-NL.jpg

27-18-LensesFocus-L.jpg

27-18-LensesFocus-NL.jpg

27-19-RodCone-L.jpg

27-19-RodCone-NL.jpg

27-20-LightPath-L.jpg

27-20-LightPath-NL.jpg

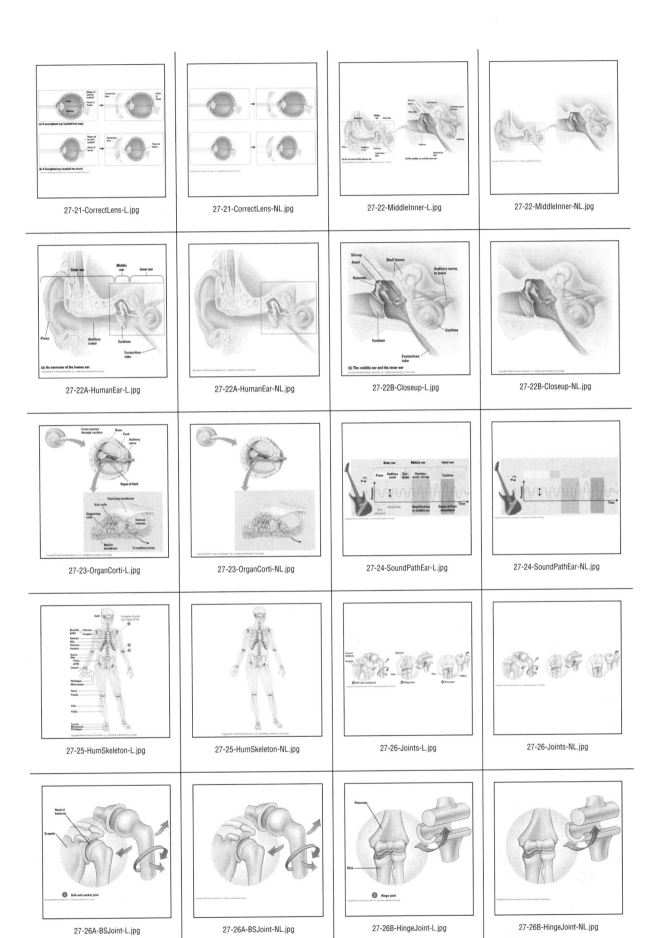

27-21-CorrectLens-L.jpg

27-21-CorrectLens-NL.jpg

27-22-MiddleInner-L.jpg

27-22-MiddleInner-NL.jpg

27-22A-HumanEar-L.jpg

27-22A-HumanEar-NL.jpg

27-22B-Closeup-L.jpg

27-22B-Closeup-NL.jpg

27-23-OrganCorti-L.jpg

27-23-OrganCorti-NL.jpg

27-24-SoundPathEar-L.jpg

27-24-SoundPathEar-NL.jpg

27-25-HumSkeleton-L.jpg

27-25-HumSkeleton-NL.jpg

27-26-Joints-L.jpg

27-26-Joints-NL.jpg

27-26A-BSJoint-L.jpg

27-26A-BSJoint-NL.jpg

27-26B-HingeJoint-L.jpg

27-26B-HingeJoint-NL.jpg

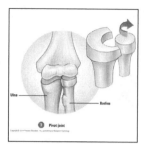
27-26C-PivotJoint-L.jpg

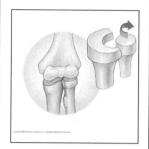
27-26C-PivotJoint-NL.jpg

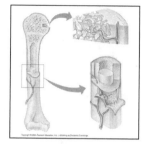
27-27-ArmBone-L.jpg

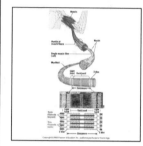
27-27-ArmBone-NL.jpg

27-28-BrokenBone.jpg

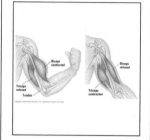
27-29-AntagMusAct-L.jpg

27-29-AntagMusAct-NL.jpg

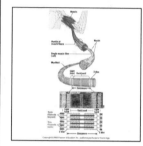
27-30-MuscleOrg-L.jpg

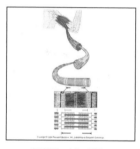
27-30-MuscleOrg-NL.jpg

27-31-MusContracAnim.mov

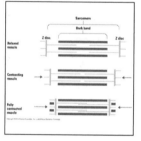
27-31-Sarcomere-L.jpg

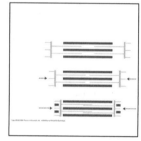
27-31-Sarcomere-NL.jpg

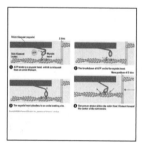
27-32-SlidFilam-L.jpg

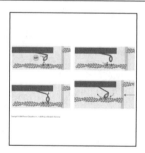
27-32-SlidFilam-NL.jpg

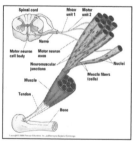
27-33-MotorUnit-L.jpg

27-33-MotorUnit-NL.jpg

27-34-Athlete.jpg

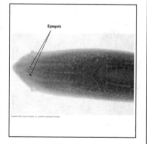
27-35-Planarian-L.jpg

27-35-Planarian-NL.jpg

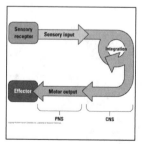
27-SK01-NervSysOrg-L.jpg

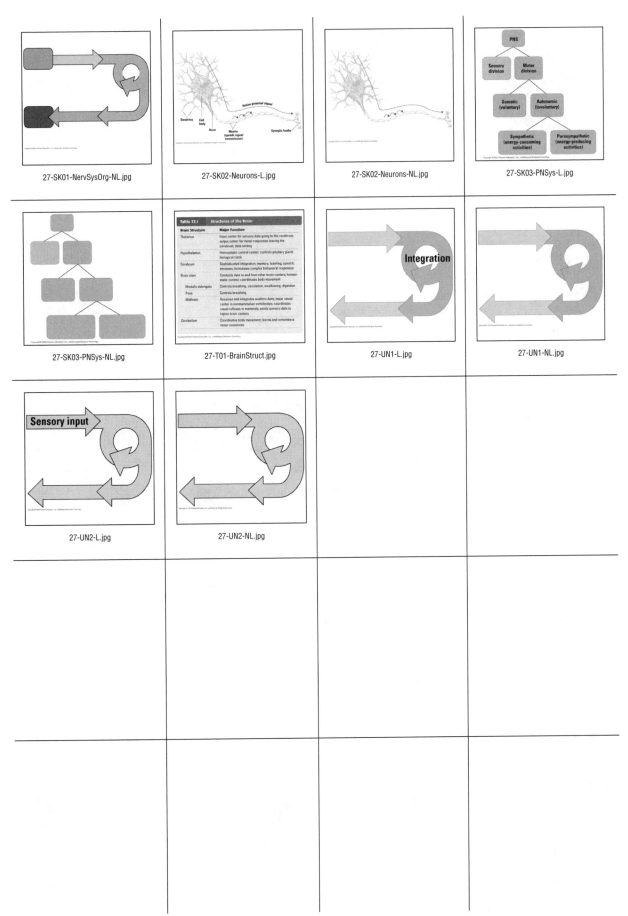

27-SK01-NervSysOrg-NL.jpg

27-SK02-Neurons-L.jpg

27-SK02-Neurons-NL.jpg

27-SK03-PNSys-L.jpg

27-SK03-PNSys-NL.jpg

27-T01-BrainStruct.jpg

27-UN1-L.jpg

27-UN1-NL.jpg

27-UN2-L.jpg

27-UN2-NL.jpg

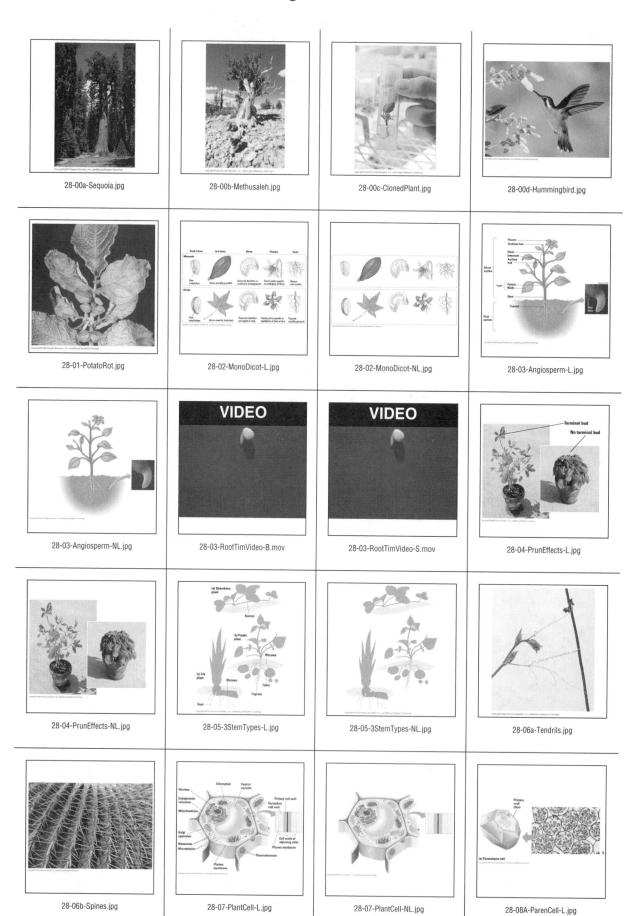

28-00a-Sequoia.jpg

28-00b-Methusaleh.jpg

28-00c-ClonedPlant.jpg

28-00d-Hummingbird.jpg

28-01-PotatoRot.jpg

28-02-MonoDicot-L.jpg

28-02-MonoDicot-NL.jpg

28-03-Angiosperm-L.jpg

28-03-Angiosperm-NL.jpg

28-03-RootTimVideo-B.mov

28-03-RootTimVideo-S.mov

28-04-PrunEffects-L.jpg

28-04-PrunEffects-NL.jpg

28-05-3StemTypes-L.jpg

28-05-3StemTypes-NL.jpg

28-06a-Tendrils.jpg

28-06b-Spines.jpg

28-07-PlantCell-L.jpg

28-07-PlantCell-NL.jpg

28-08A-ParenCell-L.jpg

28-08A-ParenCell-NL.jpg

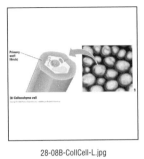

28-08B-CollCell-L.jpg

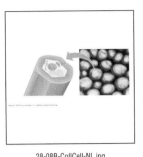

28-08B-CollCell-NL.jpg

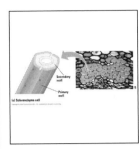

28-08C-SclerCell-L.jpg

28-08C-SclerCell-NL.jpg

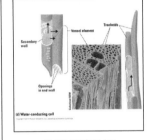

28-08D-WatrCell-L.jpg

28-08D-WatrCell-NL.jpg

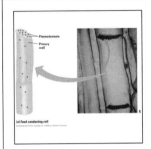

28-08E-FoodCell-L.jpg

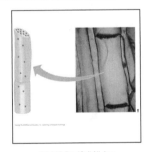

28-08E-FoodCell-NL.jpg

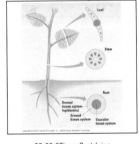

28-09-3TissueSyst-L.jpg

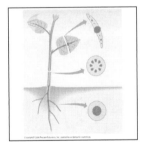

28-09-3TissueSyst-NL.jpg

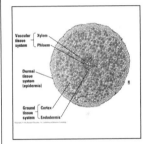

28-10-DicotRoot-L.jpg

28-10-DicotRoot-NL.jpg

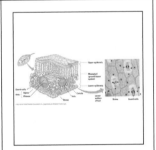

28-11-LeafTissue-L.jpg

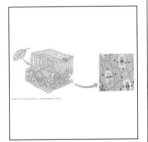

28-11-LeafTissue-NL.jpg

28-12a-GarlicBulb.jpg

28-12b-Redwoods.jpg

28-12c-Creosote.jpg

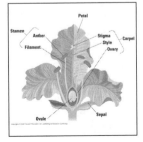

28-13-Flower-L.jpg

28-13-Flower-NL.jpg

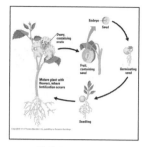

28-14-AngioCycle-L.jpg

28-14-AngioCycle-NL.jpg

28-14-AngioLfCycAnim.mov

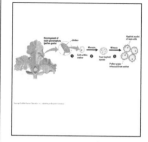

28-15-L1-PollenDevel.jpg

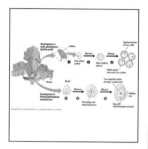

28-15-L2-Gametes-L.jpg

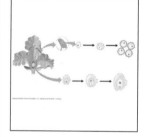

28-15-L2-Gametes-NL.jpg

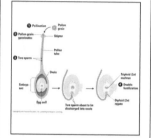

28-16-DoubleFert-L.jpg

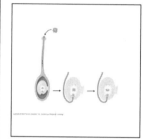

28-16-DoubleFert-NL.jpg

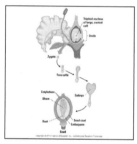

28-17-SeedDevel-L.jpg

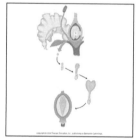

28-17-SeedDevel-NL.jpg

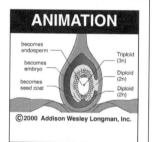

28-17-SeedDevelpAnim.mov

28-18-FruitDeveAnim.mov

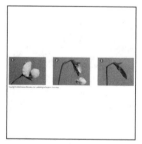

28-18-PeaPodDevel-L.jpg

28-18-PeaPodDevel-NL.jpg

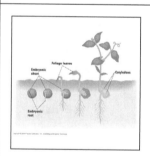

28-19-Fruit.jpg

28-20a-Germination-L.jpg

28-20a-Germination-NL.jpg

28-20b-YoungPlant.jpg

28-21a-Sequoia.jpg

28-21b-Methusaleh.jpg

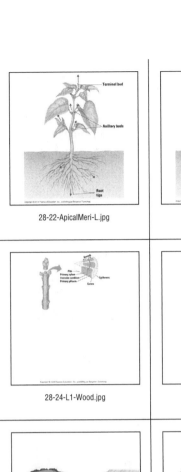

28-22-ApicalMeri-L.jpg

28-22-ApicalMeri-NL.jpg

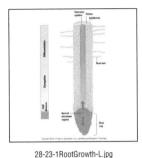

28-23-1RootGrowth-L.jpg

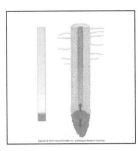

28-23-1RootGrowth-NL.jpg

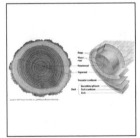

28-24-L1-Wood.jpg

28-24-L2-WoodyStem.jpg

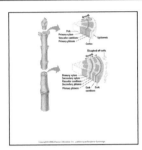

28-24-L3-2Growth-L.jpg

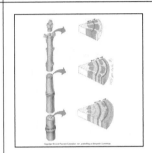

28-24-L3-2Growth-NL.jpg

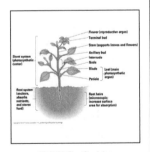

28-25-LogXsection-L.jpg

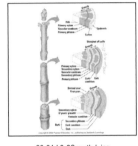

28-25-LogXsection-NL.jpg

28-26-Pollination.jpg

28-SK01-MonoDicot.jpg

28-SK02-PlantOrg-L.jpg

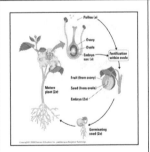

28-SK02-PlantOrg-NL.jpg

28-SK03-LifeCycle-L.jpg

28-SK03-LifeCycle-NL.jpg

29-00a-MapleSyrup.jpg

29-00b-Sunflower.jpg

29-00c-Redwoods.jpg

29-00d-MapleTree.jpg

29-01-HarvestSyrup.jpg

29-02-NutrUptake-L.jpg

29-02-NutrUptake-NL.jpg

29-02-SunDTrpVideo-B.mov

29-02-SunDTrpVideo-S.mov

29-03-Redwoods.jpg

29-04-NrichSoil.jpg

29-05a-HealthyPlant.jpg

29-05b-Ndeficiency.jpg

29-05c-Pdeficiency.jpg

29-05d-Kdeficiency.jpg

29-06-RootHairs.jpg

29-07-Mycorrhiza-L.jpg

29-07-Mycorrhiza-NL.jpg

29-08-Nbacteria-L.jpg

29-08-Nbacteria-NL.jpg

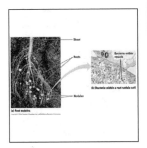

29-09-RootNodules-L.jpg

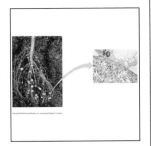

29-09-RootNodules-NL.jpg

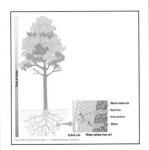

29-10-L1-WaterUptake.jpg

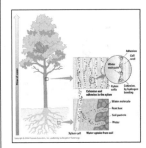

29-10-L2-XylemFlow.jpg

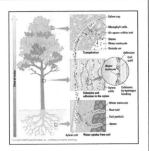

29-10-L3-H2Oflow-L.jpg

29-10-L3-H2Oflow-NL.jpg

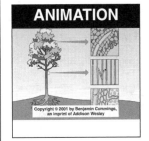

29-10-WatrFlwTreAnim.mov

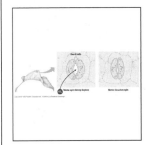

29-11-GuardCells-L.jpg

29-11-GuardCells-NL.jpg

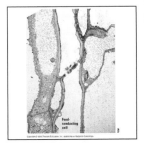

29-12-Phloem-L.jpg

29-12-Phloem-NL.jpg

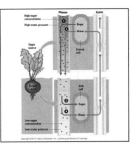

29-13-PressureFlo-L.jpg

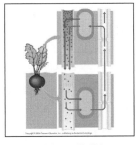

29-13-PressureFlo-NL.jpg

29-14-Phototropism.jpg

29-14-PhototroVideo-B.mov

29-14-PhototroVideo-S.mov

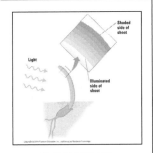

29-15-Phototrop-L.jpg

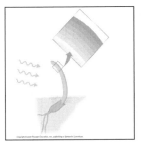

29-15-Phototrop-NL.jpg

29-16-Ethylene-L.jpg

29-16-Ethylene-NL.jpg

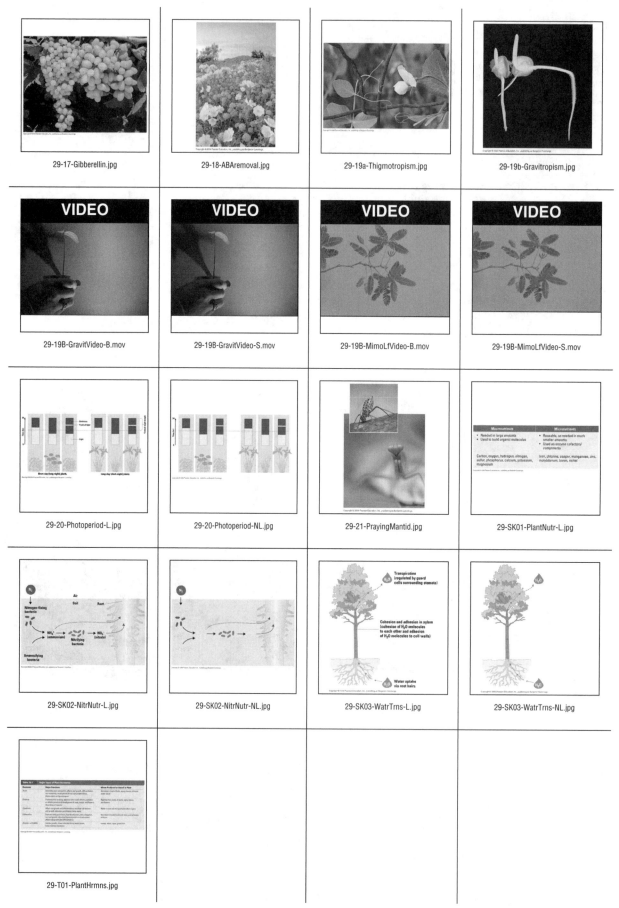

29-17-Gibberellin.jpg

29-18-ABAremoval.jpg

29-19a-Thigmotropism.jpg

29-19b-Gravitropism.jpg

29-19B-GravitVideo-B.mov

29-19B-GravitVideo-S.mov

29-19B-MimoLfVideo-B.mov

29-19B-MimoLfVideo-S.mov

29-20-Photoperiod-L.jpg

29-20-Photoperiod-NL.jpg

29-21-PrayingMantid.jpg

29-SK01-PlantNutr-L.jpg

29-SK02-NitrNutr-L.jpg

29-SK02-NitrNutr-NL.jpg

29-SK03-WatrTrns-L.jpg

29-SK03-WatrTrns-NL.jpg

29-T01-PlantHrmns.jpg

Appendix A: Animation List

Title	Animation File Name
Ionic Bonds Animation	02-08-IonicBondsAnim.mov
Covalent Bonds Animation	02-09-CovalentBondsAnim.mov
Macromolecules Animation	03-07-MacromoleculesAnim.mov
Disaccharides Animation	03-11-DisaccharidesAnim.mov
Polysaccharides Animation	03-13-PolysaccharidesAnim.mov
Fats Animation	03-15-FatsAnim.mov
Contractile Proteins Animation	03-18-ContractProteinsAnim.mov
Defensive Proteins Animation	03-18-DefensiveProteinsAnim.mov
Enzymes Animation	03-18-EnzymesAnim.mov
Signal Proteins Animation	03-18-SignalProteinsAnim.mov
Storage Proteins Animation	03-18-StorageProteinsAnim.mov
Structural Proteins Animation	03-18-StructuralProtAnim.mov
Transport Proteins Animation	03-18-TransportProtAnim.mov
Protein Structure Introduction Animation	03-21-ProteinStructureAnim.mov
Primary Protein Structure Animation	03-23A-PrimaryStructureAnim.mov
Secondary Protein Structure Animation	03-23B-SecondStructureAnim.mov
Tertiary Protein Structure Animation	03-23C-TertiaryStructureAnim.mov
Quaternary Protein Structure Animation	03-23D-QuatStructureAnim.mov
Membrane Structure Animation	04-07A-MembraneStrucAnim.mov
Receptor Proteins Animation	04-08-ReceptorProtAnim.mov
Lysosome Formation Animation	04-14-LysosomeFormAnim.mov
Endomembrane System Animation	04-16-EndomembraneSysAnim.mov
Cilia and Flagella Animation	04-20-CiliaFlagellaAnim.mov
Anchoring Junctions Animation	04-22-AnchorJunctionsAnim.mov
Communicating Junctions Animation	04-22-CommJunctionsAnim.mov
Tight Junctions Animation	04-22-TightJunctionsAnim.mov
Energy Concepts Animation	05-02-EnergyConceptsAnim.mov
How Enzymes Work Animation	05-09-HowEnzymesWorkAnim.mov
Diffusion Animation	05-11-DiffusionAnim.mov
Osmosis Animation	05-12-OsmosisAnim.mov
Active Transport Animation	05-15-ActiveTransportAnim.mov

Title	Animation File Name
Exocytosis/Endocytosis Introduction Animation	05-16-ExocytEndoIntroAnim.mov
Exocytosis Animation	05-16-ExocytosisAnim.mov
Phagocytosis Animation	05-17-PhagocytosisAnim.mov
Receptor-Mediated Endocytosis Animation	05-18-ReceptMedEndoAnim.mov
Glycolysis Animation	06-08-GlycolysisAnim.mov
Krebs Cycle Animation	06-11-KrebsCycleAnim.mov
Electron Transport Animation	06-12-ElectronTransportAnim.mov
Light Reactions Animation	07-11-LightReactionsAnim.mov
Calvin Cycle Animation	07-13-CalvinCycleAnim.mov
DNA Packing Animation	08-04-DNApackingAnim.mov
Mitosis Overview Animation	08-07a-MitosisOverviewAnim.mov
Late Interphase Animation	08-07b-LateInterphaseAnim.mov
Prophase Animation	08-07c-ProphaseAnim.mov
Late Prophase Animation	08-07d-LateProphaseAnim.mov
Metaphase Animation	08-07e-MetaphaseAnim.mov
Anaphase Animation	08-07f-AnaphaseAnim.mov
Telophase Animation	08-07g-TelophaseAnim.mov
Cytokinesis Animation	08-07h-CytokinesisAnim.mov
Interphase I Animation	08-15a-InterphaseIAnim.mov
Prophase I Animation	08-15b-ProphaseIAnim.mov
Metaphase I Animation	08-15c-MetaphaseIAnim.mov
Anaphase I Animation	08-15d-AnaphaseIAnim.mov
Telophase I & Cytokinesis Animation	08-15e-TelophaseICytokAnim.mov
Meiosis II & Cytokinesis Animation	08-15f-MeiosisIICytokAnim.mov
Crossing Over Animation	08-18-CrossingOverAnim.mov
DNA Structure Animation (big, no narration)	10-05-DNAstructAnim-B.mov
DNA Structure Animation (small)	10-05-DNAstructAnim-S.mov
DNA Replication Overview Animation	10-06-DNArepOverviewAnim.mov
DNA Replication Animation (big, no narration)	10-08-DNArepliAnim-B.mov
DNA Replication Animation (small)	10-08-DNArepliAnim-S.mov
Transcription Animation	10-13-TranscriptionAnim.mov
RNA Processing Animation	10-14-RNAprocessingAnim.mov
Translation Animation	10-18-TranslationAnim.mov
Phage T2 Reproductive Cycle Animation	10-25-PhageT2ReproAnim.mov

Title	Animation File Name
Phage Lambda Reproductive Cycles Animation	10-26-PhageReproAnim.mov
HIV Reproduction Animation	10-30-HIVreproductionAnim.mov
Leading Strand Animation (big, no narration)	10x1-LeadingStrandAnim-B.mov
Leading Strand Animation (small)	10x1-LeadingStrandAnim-S.mov
Lagging Strand Animation (big, no narration)	10x2-LaggingStrandAnim-B.mov
Lagging Strand Animation (small)	10x2-LaggingStrandAnim-S.mov
Lagging Strand Animation (big, no narration)	10x3-LaggingStrandAnim-B.mov
Lagging Strand Animation (small)	10x3-LaggingStrandAnim-S.mov
Turning on a Gene Animation	11-13-TrngOnGeneAnim.mov
Control of Translation Animation	11-16-CntrlTransAnim.mov
Protein Processing Animation	11-16-ProtProdAnim.mov
Cell Signaling Animation	11-17-CellSignlAnim.mov
Signal-Transduction Pathway Animation	11-17-SignlTrnsdAnim.mov
Head-Tail Axis Fruit Fly Animation	11-22-HTFrutFlyAnim.mov
Cloning a Gene Animation	12-09-ClonGeneAnim.mov
Restriction Enzymes Animation	12-10-RestEnzyAnim.mov
Paedomorhosis Animation	14-17-PaedomorphAnim.mov
Geologic Time Scale Animation	14-18-GeolTimScalAnim.mov
Classification Schemes Animation	14-27-ClassificAnim.mov
Geologic Time Scale Animation	14-T01-GeolTmSclAnim.mov
Macroevolution Animation	14-T01-MacroevoAnim.mov
Moss Life Cycle Animation	16-10-MossLfCycAnim.mov
Fern Life Cycle Animation	16-11-FrnLfeCycAnim.mov
Pine Life Cycle Animation	16-15-PineLfCycAnim.mov
Fungus Life Cycle Animation	16-21-FungLfeCycAnim.mov
Bowman's Capsule Animation	21-17-BowCapsulAnim.mov
Collecting Duct Animation	21-17-CollDuctAnim.mov
Effect of ADH Animation	21-17-EffectADHAnim.mov
Loop of Henle Animation	21-17-LoopHenleAnim.mov
Nephron Introduction Animation	21-17-NephrIntrAnim.mov
Antibodies Animation	24-10-AntibodsAnim.mov
Role of B Cells Animation	24-11-RoleBCellAnim.mov
Helper T Cells Animation	24-13-HelpTCellAnim.mov
Cytotoxic T Cells Animation	24-14-CytoxTCellAnim.mov

Title	Animation File Name
Nonsteroid Hormone Animation	25-03-NonstrHormAnim.mov
Steroid Hormone Animation	25-04-SterodHormAnim.mov
Female Reproductive Anatomy Animation	26-04-FemReprodAnim.mov
Male Reproductive Anatomy Animation	26-07-MaleHormAnim.mov
Male Hormones Animation	26-07-MaleReprodAnim.mov
Ovulation Animation	26-10-OvulationAnim.mov
Post Ovulation Animation	26-10-PostOvulaAnim.mov
Action Potential Animation	27-04-ActnPotentAnim.mov
Resting Potential Animation	27-04-RestPotentAnim.mov
Synapse Animation	27-06-SynapseAnim.mov
Muscle Contraction Animation	27-31-MusContracAnim.mov
Angiosperm Life Cycle Animation	28-14-AngioLfCycAnim.mov
Seed Development Animation	28-17-SeedDevelpAnim.mov
Fruit Development Animation	28-18-FruitDeveAnim.mov
Water Flow Up a Tree Animation	29-10-WatrFlwTreAnim.mov

Appendix B: Video Scripts and Credits

B = Big-format video (640 x 480)
S = Small-format video (320 x 240)

Sea Horse Video

01-14-SeaHorsesVideo-B

01-14-SeaHorsesVideo-S

The pygmy sea horses in this clip were filmed in Lembeh Straight in Indonesia. They are seen in their habitat among a distinctive type of coral. The sea horses look very much like the coral, which might serve as camouflage, or to lure prey into the seeming safety of the branching coral. Darwinian theory says that better-camouflaged sea horses have better reproductive success, and thus pass on more of the genes underlying the camouflage pattern. This would account for the evolution of the striking likeness between this pygmy sea horse and its habitat.

Credit: National Geographic

Cytoplasmic Streaming Video

04-06-CytoplasmStreVideo-B

04-06-CytoplasmStreVideo-S

Elodea is a water plant with thin leaves two cell layers thick. This view focuses at 1000x magnification midway through this layer of cells. The central space of each cell is occupied by a huge central vacuole, around which cytoplasmic streaming is observed. In the stream of cytosol, mitochondria can be seen. Chloroplasts, the larger, pigmented organelles, are also streaming, but they don't move as freely because of their size.

Credit: Michael Clayton, University of Wisconsin, Madison

Paramecium Vacuole Video

04-15A-ParameVacVideo-B

04-15A-ParameVacVideo-S

The single celled ciliated protozoan *Paramecium* is found in fresh water. It continually pulls water in by osmosis. A specialized organelle, the contractile vacuole, collects water from the cell and pumps it out with regular contractions. Two such contractions can be seen in this video clip.

Credit: Henry Mainwaring, Western Carolina University

Paramecium Cilia Video

04-20-ParamecCiliaVideo-B

04-20-ParamecCiliaVideo-S

Locomotion in the protists occurs either by the beating of hair-like structures (cilia or flagella), or by means of pseudopodia in a movement called amoeboid movement. In *Paramecium,* movement is accomplished by the coordinated beating by many short hair- like appendages called cilia. The cilia form longitudinal rows along the entire body of the cell and into the oral groove. Forward and backward movement is easily accomplished by the beating of the cilia. The beating action of the cilia produces a slow

rotation of the *Paramecium* as it moves through the water. The cilia in the oral groove propel food particles to the bottom of the gullet where the food can be ingested by phagocytosis.
Credit: Courtesy of Graham R. Kent and Rebecca L. Turner, Smith College

Plasmolyzing *Elodea* Video

05-13-PlasmoElodeaVideo-B
05-13-PlasmoElodeaVideo-S
In this clip, a leaf of the pondweed *Elodea* has been placed in a concentrated solution of table salt. A process called plasmolysis occurs as the cells lose water to the surrounding environment through osmosis. The cell contents collapse as the plasma membrane pulls away from the cell wall.
Credit: Henry Mainwaring, Western Carolina University

Elodea Video

05-13-TurgidElodeaVideo-B
05-13-TurgidElodeaVideo-S
Elodea is a water plant with thin leaves two cell layers thick. This 1000x magnified view focuses through several adjacent cells in a leaf. In the lower cell, you can clearly see a nucleus, with the smaller nucleolus inside it. The huge central vacuole is obvious in the middle cell, based on the absence of any detail in the area occupied by this organelle. Mitochondria are visible in the stream of cytosol as it sweeps around the cell. Because this is viewed using Nomarski optics, textural relief is seen—for example, the chloroplasts have visible internal structure due to the stacks of membranes in the grana.
Credit: Michael Clayton, University of Wisconsin, Madison

Hydra Budding Video

08-02-HydraBuddingVideo-B
08-02-HydraBuddingVideo-S
Hydra is capable of reproducing asexually in a process called budding, and sexually by the production of egg and sperm. The hydra in the opening scene of the video is growing a young bud close to its base. Buds form as an outgrowth of the two-layered body wall. At first the tentacles are relatively short and the gastrovascular cavity of the parent and the young bud are continuous. As the bud reaches maturity the tentacles elongate and the gastrovascular cavity becomes separate. Eventually the bud pinches off and drops to the substratum to begin independent life.
Credit: Courtesy of Graham R. Kent and Rebecca L. Turner, Smith College

Animal Mitosis Video

08-07-AnimalMitosisVideo-B
08-07-AnimalMitosisVideo-S
In this time-lapse video of cell division in a newt lung cell, you will see a process that normally takes more than an hour occur in less than a minute. This newt cell has already started prophase, the first stage of mitosis. Chromosomes have condensed and become clearly visible, contained within the nuclear envelope. In the cytoplasm, the mitotic spindle begins to form during prophase. During prometaphase, the nuclear envelope breaks up. The chromosomes become even shorter and thicker. The microtubules

of the mitotic spindle attach to the chromosomes and move them toward the equator of the cell. In metaphase, the chromosomes convene at the metaphase plate, an imaginary plane equidistant from the spindle poles. In this video, we can clearly see that each chromosome consists of two sister chromatids, joined at a centromere. Anaphase begins when the paired centromeres of each chromosome separate and the chromatids—now full-fledged chromosomes—are moved to the poles. At the same time, the poles of the cell are moved apart, stretching the cell. During telophase, two daughter nuclei form at the poles of the cell. Nuclear envelopes form around the gathered chromosomes, and the chromosomes become less tightly coiled. In the nuclei nucleoli appear and in the cytoplasm the spindle breaks up. Cytokinesis begins during telophase. In animal cells, a cleavage furrow forms, pinching the cell in two and separating the two identical daughter cells.
Credit: Conly L. Rieder, NY State Department of Health

Human Fetus Ultrasound Video #1

09-01-Ultrasound1Video-B
09-01-Ultrasound1Video-S
Ultrasound imaging uses high frequency sound waves to create a picture of a growing fetus. This ultrasound was performed when the mother was about 20 weeks pregnant.
Credit: Courtesy of Mike and Charlie McCullough

Human Fetus Ultrasound Video #2

09-01-Ultrasound2Video-B
09-01-Ultrasound2Video-S
Ultrasound uses very high frequency sound waves of between 3.5 to 7.0 megahertz (i.e., 3.5 to 7 million cycles per second) that are emitted from a transducer. When the beams of ultrasound hit the various tissues inside the body the differences in the density of the material produces a variety of reflected sound that can be collected and formed into an image. This image is really a two-dimensional "slice" through the patient. The video shows various views of the fetus (now a beautiful baby!) sucking her thumb, kicking, turning over, etc. In an obstetric ultrasound examination the transducer is placed against the abdomen of the patient to form images of the developing fetus and gather information about gestational age, fetal size, and heart beat. Also, malformations in the fetus can be assessed and measurements can be made accurately on the images displayed on the screen. The video shows how the length of the foot can be measured (2.75 cm in this case). The doppler shift principle can be used in ultrasound to accurately measure the blood flow in the fetal blood vessels and monitor the heart function. This, coupled to the use of "color flow" mapping, can clearly depict the flow of blood in fetal blood vessels in a scan, the direction of the flow being represented by different colors. The video shows high rates of flow in red, and low rates in blue.
Credit: Courtesy of Graham R. Kent and Rebecca L. Turner, Smith College

Scientists Working in Molecular Biology Lab Video

11-04A-ScieWkVideo-B
This series of clips shows several standard procedures that are often performed in a molecular biology laboratory. In the first clip, the scientist is sterilely picking bacterial cells from a particular colony on an agar plate. In the second, she is treating the cells with several solutions in a procedure to isolate plasmid DNA (containing cloned DNA)

from the cells. In the third, she is loading the isolated and digested DNA into the wells of an agarose gel, where it will be subjected to gel electrophoresis. The pattern of bands in each lane can be photographed with a digital camera and analyzed on a computer (seen in the fourth clip), to begin to characterize the cloned stretch of DNA. With the advent of sequencing and analyzing entire genomes, much of the sequencing operation has been automated. Here we see various robotic machines processing DNA samples for analysis.
Credit: Courtesy of Genencor International, Inc.

Dome-Backed Tortoise Video

13-04-TortoiseVideo-B
13-04-TortoiseVideo-S
These Dome-Backed Tortoises are found on Santa Cruz Island. The Galápagos giant tortoise, *Geochelone elephantopus,* exists in only 11 subspecies found on seven of the Galápagos Islands. In addition to the domed variety, tortoises with an upswept "saddle-back" carapace (shell) are also found. It has been said that natives can tell which island a tortoise is from by the shape of its shell. The tortoise shown here could be anywhere from 50–150 years old or more and might weigh as much as 500 pounds when fully grown. The giant tortoise is a vegetarian, eating over fifty varieties of island plants. Many of the populations of giant tortoise are not large and their survival is in danger.
Credit: Richard Benz, Wyckliffe School

Galápagos Islands Overview Video

13-04-GalapagosVideo-B
13-04-GalapagosVideo-S
There are 13 main islands and 14 smaller islands in the Galápagos Archipelago. Here we are approaching Isabella Island, a volcanic island and the largest of the islands. Isabella is on the western edge of the Galápagos Archipelago and is one of the newest islands in the group. This large island is made up of six volcanoes, five of which have been recently active. Wisps of volcanic smoke can sometimes be seen coming from some of the active vents. Many of the Galápagos species can be found on Isabella including marine iguanas, five subspecies of giant tortoise, Galápagos Sea Lions and ten species of Galápagos finches.
Credit: Richard Benz, Wyckliffe School

Marine Iguana Video

13-04-MarIguanaVideo-B
13-04-MarIguanaVideo-S
The marine iguana, *Amblyrhynchus cristatus,* is found throughout the Galápagos Islands. These marine iguanas are found on Fernandina Island. They are the only marine-going iguanas in the world. Fernandina Island supports large populations of marine iguanas. This ocean-going reptile is noted for diving and eating algae off the submerged volcanic rocks. In this clip, you can see this iguana eating algae off the rocks. Only the largest animals actually dive for their algae. Most eat algae from shallow inter-tidal rocks or exposed reefs. Much of the day is spent resting and digesting. The iguana needs to gather its body heat from the sun and the warm volcanic rocks.
Credit: Richard Benz, Wyckliffe School

Galápagos Sea Lion Video

13-04-SeaLionVideo-B

13-04-SeaLionVideo-S

The Galápagos Sea Lion, *Zalophus wollibacki,* is a subspecies of the California Sea Lion, *Zalophus califorianus.* It is the largest terrestrial animal in the islands. The Galápagos Sea Lion is often found in large groups called colonies. Large males form harems of groups of 15 or 20 females. (These are not true harems since the females are free to wander from one grouping to another.) In this clip we see a small family grouping of sea lions. The barking one is the young bull, there is one cow, and a youngster. This group of sea lions is on Fernandina Island.

Credit: Richard Benz, Wyckliffe School

Grand Canyon Video

13-07-GrndCanVideo-B

13-07-GrndCanVideo-S

This footage was filmed from an airplane flying over the Grand Canyon in Arizona. The Colorado River, seen at the bottom, has formed this magnificent canyon by gradual erosion over the past nine million years. The layers, or strata, of sedimentary rocks are clearly visible, with the oldest at the bottom. By analyzing fossils from each stratum, we have learned much about changes in diversity of life forms. Changes in the course of the river have led to specific land formations such as the bluffs seen to the left. The idea that we could ascribe various land forms, such as canyons, to mechanisms currently operating, such as erosion by rivers, was first proposed by Scottish geologist James Hutton near the beginning of the 19th century.

Credit: Courtesy of USGS

Lava Flow Video

14-20-LavaFlowVideo-B

14-20-LavaFlowVideo-S

This video clip shows lava flowing from a region of volcanic activity. The molten rock will eventually cool, defining new features of the landscape. Volcanoes and lava flows are a graphic reminder that the form of land masses on the earth continues to change over time.

Credit: Courtesy of USGS

Volcanic Eruption Video

14-20-VolcErptVideo-B

14-20-VolcErptVideo-S

In this footage, we are looking into the top of the Pu'u O'o volcano in Hawaii. In a volcanic eruption, steam and other gases deep inside the earth explode outward, shooting molten rock through an opening. Over time, the cooled, hardened rock, as well as cinders and ashes, pile up into a cone-shaped mountain with a depression at the top (the crater). In this particular crater, molten rock is visible, the hottest of which glows red. Volcanoes, like earthquakes, tend to occur at boundaries where two moving tectonic plates abut against each other. Volcanoes that occur under the ocean can form islands. A good example are the Galápagos Islands off the coast of South America, where Darwin made observations leading to his theory of natural selection and evolution.

Credit: Courtesy of USGS

Oscillatoria Video

15-11-OscillaVideo-B
15-11-OscillaVideo-S
Shown in this movie are three filamentous bacteria from the domain Bacteria, specifically the group known as Cyanobacteria (previously the blue-green algae). This species is named *Oscillatoria*, and you can see a short filament moving along and around a much longer one in a gliding motion that has been called "barber-poling". These bacteria do not have flagella, and the molecular basis for their motility remains somewhat of a mystery.
Credit: Michael Clayton, University of Wisconsin, Madison

Prokaryotic Flagella *(Salmonella typhimurium)* Video

15-12-SalFlagVideo-S
This is a dark field video of bacterial cells of the species *Salmonella typhimurium*, filmed with a full intensity beam. Due to light scattering, the cells appear greater than their actual size, and the flagellum on each cell can be seen clearly. Many bacteria swim by rotating their flagella in a helical manner. In media of normal viscosity, the flagella are moving too fast for their helical waveform to be seen. In the second half of the clip, the cells are placed in a highly viscous medium. The flagellar rotation is now slow enough for the waveform to be seen easily. The direction of rotation can be changed, and thus the cells are able to change their direction. Flagellar motion is accomplished by means of a set of proteins that act together as a motor, fueled by a proton gradient across the cell membrane.
Credit: Robert Macnab, Professor of Molecular Biophysics and Biochemistry at Yale University

Euglena Video #1

15-18-Euglna1Video-B
15-18-Euglna1Video-S
The *Euglena acus* in this clip was treated with $NiSO_4$. Nickel ion paralyzes the flagellum. We can see the extreme shape changes of the cell, showing clearly the great flexibility of the pellicle, or specialized cell membrane. You can see the paralyzed anterior flagellum, at the left end of the cell throughout most of this clip. At the anterior end, you can see the reddish spot which functions as a light detector.
Credit: Michael Clayton, University of Wisconsin, Madison

Euglena Video #2

15-18-Euglna2Video-B
15-18-Euglna2Video-S
Seen here are two protistan cells of the species *Euglena acus*. This species is in the euglenoid group of the clade Euglenozoa. *Euglena* and closely related protists are characterized by having a pocket at the anterior end from which emerges a flagellum. In this clip, the use of phase contrast microscopy allows us to view the flagellum at the anterior (rounded) end. The posterior end is more pointed. These cells are anchored at the posterior end by nail polish, and you can see their swimming behavior. The small specks swarming around them are bacteria, which allows you to see the relative size of prokaryotes and eukaryotic protists.
Credit: Michael Clayton, University of Wisconsin, Madison

Stentor Video #1 and #2

15-19-Stent1Video-B
15-19-Stent1Video-S
15-19-Stent2Video-B
15-19-Stent2Video-S

Stentor is a large trumpet-shaped cell that is covered with cilia that permits the cell to move around. Usually *Stentor* is observed while it is attached to the substrate by its base and the cell can wave back and forth in search of food particles. At the fluted end of the cell are the membranelles which are short finlike structures whose beating sets up a current in which food particles are brought to the organism's "mouth." Ingestion is by phagocytosis. The videos show small food particles being swept into the mouth region; however, large food particles are rejected by the cell.
Credit: Courtesy of Graham R. Kent and Rebecca L. Turner, Smith College (Stentor1) and Michael Clayton, University of Wisconsin, Madison (Stentor2)

Vorticella Video #1

15-19-Vortic1Video-B
15-19-Vortic1Video-S

Vorticella is a member of the ciliated protists, but the body has few cilia. Surrounding the "mouth" are three rows of cilia that wind in counter-clockwise direction toward the mouth. The bell-shaped body normally remains attached to the substrate by a coiled stalk that is able to contract and extend itself while the organism searches for food. The video shows how the beating cilia sets up a distinctive counter-clockwise current that draws food particles to the mouth of the cell. Ingestion is by phagocytosis.
Credit: Courtesy of Graham R. Kent and Rebecca L. Turner, Smith College

Vorticella Video #2

15-19-Vortic2Video-B
15-19-Vortic2Video-S

This clip shows the ciliated protist *Vorticella*. This species is a suspension feeder, with bands of ciliary membranes surrounding the apical end (shown here at the right). Movement of these membranes serves to create water currents and sweep food parti-cles, such as bacterial cells, into the buccal cavity and from there into the forming food vacuole. This particular species has a bell-shaped body on a long slender stalk. Within the body covering of the stalk lie bundles of contractile filaments called myonemes. Contraction of the myonemes results in the popping motion shown here.
Credit: Michael Clayton, University of Wisconsin, Madison

Vorticella Video #3

15-19-Vortic3Video-B
15-19-Vortic3Video-S

This clip shows the ciliated protist *Vorticella*. As seen here, the organism is sessile, with its bell-shaped body anchored to a piece of algae by a long slender stalk. Within the body covering of the stalk lie bundles of contractile filaments called myonemes. Con-traction of the myonemes results in the popping motion shown here.
Credit: Michael Clayton, University of Wisconsin, Madison

Amoeba Pseudopodia Video #1

15-19b-AmoPs1Video-B

15-19b-AmoPs1Video-S

In this clip the pseudopodium, or false foot, is extending from the front of an amoeba using a process that involves changes in the viscosity of the cytoplasm. The inner flowing cytoplasm is called the endoplasm, and is in a liquid sol state. This flows forward filling the pseudopodium. At the front, the endoplasm is converted into the clear gellike ectoplasm, which is located just under the plasma membrane. At the rear of the amoeba, the ectoplasm is converted back into endoplasm, and it flows forward to the front of the cell to be converted back into ectoplasm.

Credit: Courtesy of Graham R. Kent and Rebecca L. Turner, Smith College

Amoeba Pseudopodia Video #2

15-19b-AmoPs2Video-B

15-19b-AmoPs2Video-S

Locomotion in rhizopods, or amoebas, occurs by means of pseudopodia in a process called amoeboid movement. *Amoeba proteus* is a large unicellular organism that moves over its substrate by sending extensions of its cytoplasm, called pseudopodia, in various directions. The pseudopodia are capable of surrounding and engulfing food by phagocytosis. Even though *Amoeba* has been one of the most intensely studied organisms, the exact mechanism of its movement is still not completely understood. However, the leading edge of the amoeba is a clear zone that seems devoid of cytoplasmic organelles; this is called the ectoplasm. The rest of the cytoplasm is called the endoplasm. Fluorescence microscopy has shown the ectoplasm contains large amounts of actin, the contractile protein common in muscle cells.

Credit: Henry Mainwaring, Western Carolina University

Plasmodial Slime Mold Streaming Video

15-21-SlmMoStVideo-B

15-21-SlmMoStVideo-S

This clip shows a piece of the plasmodial slime mold *Physarum polycephalum*. This organism does not photosynthesize, it is heterotrophic and must feed. Shown here is the feeding stage known as the plasmodium, which moves around as an amoeboid mass, engulfing its food by phagocytosis. The feeding plasmodium is a single cell containing many nuclei that have arisen by repeated mitoses of the original nucleus. The single mass of cytoplasm contains fine channels within which cytoplasm streams back and forth as can be seen in this video clip. Cytoplasmic streaming functions to distribute nutrients and oxygen to other parts of the cell, as well as helping in amoeboid movement of the plasmodium.

Credit: Michael Clayton, University of Wisconsin, Madison

Plasmodial Slime Mold Video

15-21-SlmeMldVideo-B

15-21-SlmeMldVideo-S

This clip shows an overview of the plasmodial slime mold *Physarum polycephalum*. Shown here is a feeding plasmodium, a single cell containing many nuclei that have arisen by repeated mitoses of the original nucleus. As the magnification increases,

details of the branching structure are visible. This stage is shown at much higher magnification in a separate clip, Plasmodial Slime Mold Streaming Video.
Credit: Michael Clayton, University of Wisconsin, Madison

Dinoflagellate Video

15-22A-DinoflVideo-B
15-22A-DinoflVideo-S
Locomotion in the protists occurs either by the beating of hair-like structures (cilia or flagella), or by means of pseudopodia in a process called amoeboid movement. Compared to the cell's body length, flagella are long and are less numerous than cilia. Most flagellated cells have only one or two flagella. Motility in *Peridinium* is typical of many dinoflagellates. There is a posterior flagellum that provides forward motion, and a second flagellum located in a groove that wraps around or "girdles" the equatorial region of the cell. Although the girdle flagellum is difficult to see, it contributes to the cell's rotating or gyrating motion as it moves through the water. The word *dino-* comes from the Greek meaning "to whirl."
Credit: Courtesy of Graham R. Kent and Rebecca L. Turner, Smith College

Misc. Diatoms Video #1

15-22B-MiDia1Video-B
15-22B-MiDia1Video-S
This clip shows motile pennate diatoms of the species *Navicula,* collected from the Maunesha River in Wisconsin, just after the winter ice melted in March, 2001. Diatoms are possibly the most important primary producers in the aquatic environment. Each cell is enclosed in two valves, like the top and bottom of a petri dish. There are two classes of diatoms, based on the shape of their valves when viewed straight on. <u>Centric</u> diatoms are radially symmetric, while <u>pennate</u> diatoms are bilaterally symmetric, as seen here for *Navicula.* The cells in this clip appearing more pointed at the ends and wider in the middle are viewed from straight on at one valve, whereas the ones appearing more uniform in width with blunter ends are seen from the side. The latter is called the "girdle view" because it shows the girdle, a longitudinal trough in the side of the cell wall thought to be involved in motility of these cells. Going across the right side of the screen you can also see an example of the motility of the filamentous cyanobacterium *Oscillatoria.*
Credit: Michael Clayton, University of Wisconsin, Madison

Misc. Diatoms Video #2

15-22B-MiDia2Video-B
15-22B-MiDia2Video-S
Seen on this clip is the motility of several species of aquatic organisms collected from the Maunesha River in Wisconsin, just after the ice melted. We can recognize four species, including two pennate diatoms. The smaller one is *Navicula* sp., while the longer more slender one is *Nitzchia* sp. Three filaments of the cyanobacterium *Oscillatoria* are also seen, as well as the eukaryotic green alga *Spirogyra,* the bright green filament on the upper left.
Credit: Michael Clayton, University of Wisconsin, Madison

Volvox Colony Video

15-22D-VolColVideo-B
15-22D-VolColVideo-S

This footage focuses through a colony of *Volvox,* a colonial green alga, at 200x magnification. While *Chlamydomonas* is most closely related to primitive ancestors of the Volvocine line, *Volvox* is the most recently evolved. *Chlamydomonas* is unicellular, while other members of this phylogenetic group can be thought of as multicellular versions of *Chlamydomonas.* A *Volvox* colony is a hollow sphere, made up of 128 or 256 cells embedded in a gelatinous matrix. The cells are usually connected to each other by strands of cytoplasm. In structure, each single cell resembles *Chlamydomonas* in having two flagella and a single cup-shaped chloroplast. This footage focuses down and back up through a colony. At first the focus is on the colony wall, then it moves through four daughter colonies inside. The first is smaller and younger, the larger three are older. All colonies have arisen from certain enlarged cells in the colony which are destined to divide to form daughter colonies.
Credit: Michael Clayton, University of Wisconsin, Madison

Volvox Flagella Video

15-22D-VolFlaVideo-B
15-22D-VolFlaVideo-S

This video clip focuses through a *Volvox* colony at 600x magnification, and back. At first, the focus is on the outer wall closest to the viewer, then it moves through a daughter colony inside to the back side of the mother colony. Finally, the focus comes back up, ending midway through the daughter colony, with the flagella of the wall cells in the daughter colony clearly visible. The structure of each cell and their cytoplasmic connections are seen even more clearly in this higher magnification view than in the previous two clips.
Credit: Michael Clayton, University of Wisconsin, Madison

Chlamydomonas Video

15-23-ChlamydVideo-B
15-23-ChlamydVideo-S

Chlamydomonas is a unicellular green alga with two anterior flagella, and a single cup-shaped chloroplast. Each cell is about 10 micrometers across. This cell is viewed with Nomarski optics, which gives an image that appears to have three-dimensional relief. The smooth space at the anterior end is the contractile vacuole, contraction of which can be seen clearly in this clip. This organelle is involved in water regulation in *Chlamydomonas.* By expelling a solution hypotonic to that in the cell, the contractile vacuole counters the osmotic movement of water into the cell. The slightly larger circular structure at the other end is the pyrenoid, within the chloroplast, where starch is deposited. The textural relief around the pyrenoid is due to the thylakoid membrane stacks in the chloroplast.
Credit: Michael Clayton, University of Wisconsin, Madison

Flowering Plant Life Cycle Time-Lapse Video

16-02-PltTimeVideo-B
16-02-PltTimeVideo-S

The video shows the growth and reproduction of a variety of the mustard plant, *Brassica rapa,* sped up 12,000 times. The seeds of flowering plants contain a young embryo

and stored food to fuel the early stages of growth. In *Brassica rapa* seeds, the food is stored in two cotyledon, or "seed leaves," which emerge first from the ground and quickly become photosynthetic. As growth progresses, the stem elongates and more leaves are produced. The appearance of flower buds signifies the plant is about to engage in sexual reproduction. Deep within the flower there are two locations where meiosis produces two types of spores. Microspores are produced in the anther sacs, and megaspores are formed in structures called ovules. Ovules are found inside the base of the carpel in a region called the ovary. Both the microspores and megaspores undergo regular cell divisions to produce small simple organisms called gametophytes. The microspores become the male gametophytes and are commonly known as pollen, whereas the megaspores develop into female gametophytes. At maturity the male gametophyte produces two sperm cells and the female gametophyte produces one egg cell. However the sexes cannot get together unless some pollinating agent moves pollen (male gametophyte) from the anther to the stigma. In this video, a small black brush is the pollinator. Now the sperm from the pollen can reach the egg cell via a pollen tube that is produced by the pollen.
Credit: Courtesy of Graham R. Kent and Rebecca L. Turner, Smith College

Flower Blooming Time-Lapse Video

16-17-FlwTimVideo-B
16-17-FlwTimVideo-S
This time-lapse video accelerates the blooming of a North American wildflower. The flower sepals and petals enclose the gamete-producing organs. The female organ is called a carpel, and the male organ is called a stamen. Once the flower has bloomed, it will attract pollen-carrying animals, such as bees and birds, thus enhancing the efficiency of reproduction. The evolution of the flower has been a major factor in accounting for the success of angiosperm plants. The coevolution of pollinators with plants is also an intriguing topic.
Credit: National Geographic

Bee Pollinating Video

16-17-BeePoVideo-B
16-17-BeePoVideo-S
Many plants rely on animals to transport pollen from the anthers to the stigma of the carpel. Typically, the pollinators are rewarded for this work with a sugary substance called nectar, and/or pollen which is high in protein. Many different animals act as pollinators—bees, beetles, butterflies, birds, bats, etc. This video shows how a bumble bee visiting a *Salvia* plant will burrow its head into the corolla of the flower to suck the nectar from the flower's nectary. The anthers of the flower are located in such a position that the bee inevitably becomes dusted with pollen. When the bee emerges from the flower it spends a few seconds using a specialized set of bristles on the first pair of legs to brush the pollen from its body and maneuver the pollen into the yellow pollen baskets located on the third pair of legs. The bee is not completely successful in removing all the pollen from its body and when the bee enters the next flower, pollen will be deposited on the sticky stigma of the carpel. For the flower, the bee is essential for allowing sexual reproduction to occur; for the bee, the flower provides a supply of sugar and pollen to manufacture honey for the hive.
Credit: Courtesy of Graham R. Kent and Rebecca L. Turner, Smith College

Bat Pollinating Agave Plant Video

16-17-BatPoVideo-B
16-17-BatPoVideo-S

This footage shows a close-up view of a branch from Palmer's agave (*Agave palmeri*), the major food plant for two species of bat in southeastern Arizona—the Mexican long-tongued bat (*Choeronycteris mexicana*) and the lesser long-nosed bat (*Leptonycteris mexicana*). *Agave palmeri* is a century plant, which grows as a rosette of spiky leaves for 8 to 35 years before blooming once, then dying. During late summer, when this footage was filmed, the bats get all their nourishment from this agave, obtaining carbohydrates from the nectar and protein and lipids from the pollen. Bats can't hover like hummingbirds can, so each visit is just as long as a few wing beats, during which they can stick their tongues out two to three times to lap up nectar. This is facilitated by hair-like projections at the end of their long tongues, helping their tongues to act like sponges. In addition, pollen from the flower gets stuck on their fur, and they later groom the pollen off of each other and ingest it. An agave branch like the one shown here can have up to 100 flowers on it, so it can sustain several bat visits per night. In this clip we see three visits.
Credit: Katharine Hinman, SUNY Stony Brook, Department of Ecology and Evolution

Allomyces Zoospore Release Video

16-21-AlmyZooVideo-S

Allomyces is an aquatic, saprotrophic fungus that is found worldwide in soil and water. It reproduces asexually by converting the contents of a sporangium into motile diploid zoospores. Here you can see one zoospore slowly squeezing out of the pore in the sporangium. This spore will swim away and attach to a suitable substrate, where it will retract the flagellum, and grow into a new diploid body or thallus under suitable conditions.
Credit: Henry Mainwaring, Western Carolina University

Phlyctochytrium Zoospore Release Video

16-21-PhlyZooVideo-B
16-21-PhlyZooVideo-S

The aquatic fungus *Phlyctochytrium* reproduces asexually by converting the entire contents of the flasked shaped body, or thallus, into flagellated zoospores. Here you can see a number of zoospores being rapidly released through a pore in the flask. These spores swim away and attach to a suitable substrate, where they retract the flagellum, and grow into a new thallus under suitable conditions.
Credit: Henry Mainwaring, Western Carolina University

Saprolegnia Oogonium Video

16-21-SapOogoVideo-B
16-21-SapOogoVideo-S

This video clip focuses down and then back up through the sexual reproductive structures in the water mold *Saprolegnia,* which can parasitize live fish or decompose dead fish and flies in the water. *Saprolegnia* is "fungal-like" in that its body is made up of hyphae, but these are coenocytic hyphae rather than septate hyphae, as would be found in true fungi such as yeasts. Coenocytic hyphae are fine branching filaments, each containing many nuclei in a common cytoplasm, rather than the nuclei being separated

by cell walls (as in septate hyphae). *Saprolegnia* reproduces both asexually, via zoo-spores, and sexually. In the sexual mode, shown here, the haploid eggs are formed within the female reproductive structure, the oogonium, which is the major spherical structure through which we focus in the middle of the screen. The four smaller struc-tures hooking into the outside of the oogonium are the male reproductive organs, called antheridia, within which haploid sperm are formed. The sperm are not flagel-lated, so they must be delivered to the eggs so fertilization can occur. Sperm are de-livered via tubes, which can be seen here if you look carefully. Fertilization has already happened in the oogonium shown here, and the four smaller circular structures inside the oogonium are the zygotes (fertilized eggs).
Credit: Michael Clayton, University of Wisconsin, Madison

Saprolegnia Zoospore Release Video

16-21-SapZooVideo-B
16-21-SapZooVideo-S
This footage shows the release of zoospores from a zoosporangium of the water mold *Saprolegnia*. In the asexual mode of reproduction, as shown here, diploid zoospores are released from a zoosporangium, formed on the end of a coenocytic hypha. At first the zoospores are biflagellated, allowing them to swim. Zoospores then become encysted, and later germinate and grow into the coenocytic hyphal form. In this clip the small specks swarming around the zoosporangium are bacterial cells.
Credit: Michael Clayton, University of Wisconsin, Madison

Earthworm Movement Video

16-20-ErthwrmVideo-B
16-20-ErthwrmVideo-S
Earthworms possess two muscle layers in their body wall. The outer or circular muscles have fibers that run around the circumference of the body. The fibers of the inner mus-cle layer are oriented along the length of the earthworm. Earthworms move by peri-staltic locomotion. Contracting the circular muscles makes the animal long and skinny, and contraction of the longitudinal muscles thickens and shortens the animal. The video shows how the worm will thicken and shorten one region of its body while the adjacent region is elongated and made skinny. The worm can push itself forward be-cause short hair-like appendages called setae are extended in the region that becomes short and fat, thereby anchoring that region of the body and allowing the adjacent an-terior region to move forward.
Credit: Courtesy of Graham R. Kent and Rebecca L. Turner, Smith College

Thimble Jellies Video

17-11-ThmbJelVideo-B
17-11-ThmbJelVideo-S
This cloud of thimble jellies (*Linuche unguiculata*), filmed in the Caribbean, are using contractile fibers derived from both of their body layers to contract their bell-shaped bodies, which allows them to move through the water. These contractile fibers are not true muscles, which are only found in animals with three tissue layers. Their move-ments are coordinated by a nerve net.
Credit: National Geographic

Hydra Eating Water Flea Time-Lapse Video

17-11-HydrEatVideo-B

17-11-HydrEatVideo-S

The opening scene shows a hydra to the right of *Daphnia,* commonly called the "water flea." Hydra are sessile animals in the phylum Cnidaria. Like most cnidarians, hydra possess a ring of tentacles that surround the mouth. The mouth leads to a gastrovascular cavity with only one opening. Hydra, like most cnidarians, have highly specialized stinging cells called nematocysts. Some of these stinging cells inject a venom that paralyzes the hydra's prey, and allows the tentacles to surround and draw the prey into the mouth. The video shows the immobilizing of the *Daphnia* and the process of ingesting the prey into the gastrovascular cavity where it is broken down into small particles that are engulfed, by phagocytosis, by the cells lining the gastrovascular cavity.

Credit: Courtesy of Graham R. Kent and Rebecca L. Turner, Smith College

Hydra Releasing Sperm Video

17-11A-HySperVideo-B

17-11A-HySperVideo-S

It is common knowledge that hydra, the small, freshwater cnidarian, reproduces asexually by budding. Under certain environmental conditions, hydra produce gametes and reproduce sexually as well. Looking at the whole organism you can see *Hydra vulgaris* with several breast-shaped spermaries, or testes. In the second, closer shot you can see the hydra spermary. And then, finally, you can see the hydra sperm being released from spermary.

Credit: Courtesy of Kerry Thompson

Jelly Swimming Video

17-11B-JelSwmVideo-B

17-11B-JelSwmVideo-S

This is a "moon jelly" (Class Scyphozoa), *Aurelia aurita.* These jellies are quite common along the Atlantic coast of the U.S. and the Bahamas. The medusa form, shown here, predominates in the jelly life cycle. As members of the phylum Cnidaria, jellies have only two layers of tissue, separated by an acellular layer called the mesoglea. The gelatinous consistency of the mesoglea gives jellies their name. The tentacles seen hanging downward contain nematocysts, stinging cells capable of being discharged upon contact with another organism. Toxins in the nematocysts are capable of paralyzing prey, so that they can be ingested as food through the centrally located mouth and digested in the baglike gastrovascular cavity. The four white rings in the center of the bell are the gonads, where the gametes will form. Jellies can reproduce either asexually by budding or sexually.

Credit: National Geographic

C. elegans Crawling Video

17-16-CelegCraVideo-B

17-16-CelegCraVideo-S

Caenorhabditis elegans, or *C. elegans,* is a species of nematode (roundworm) that normally lives in the soil and eats bacteria. The worm shown here is crawling on an agar plate in a lab, demonstrating movements similar to those it would normally use to move through the soil. Structures and organs in this worm are clearly visible, and some

of them are labeled in this clip. Because an adult of this species is made up of only about 1000 cells, and they are easy to raise in a lab, *C. elegans* has become a popular species for the study of embryonic development. The adult shown here, like most adult *C. elegans,* is a self-fertilizing hermaphrodite: each adult produces both sperm and eggs, and fertilization is internal. Adult hermaphrodites are one millimeter long.
Credit: Robert P. Goldstein, UNC Chapel Hill

C. elegans Development Time-Lapse Video

17-16-CelegDevVideo-S

C. elegans, the soil worm or nematode, is a useful species for the study of embryonic development because the lineage and fates of all cells are known, and also genetic techniques can be used to determine the function of specific genes. This time-lapse film shows the first 15 hours of development from a fertilized egg to a fully formed worm. The fertilized egg is about 50 microns long (1/20th of a millimeter), and contains two nuclei. The nucleus on the right is from the egg; the one on the left was contributed by the sperm at fertilization. This one cell will divide into all the cell types of the embryo, including muscle cells, nerve cells, gut cells, etc. The fates of some cells are determined quite early. For example, at 00:56:01 (hours:minutes:seconds of real time) there are eight cells. The cell on the lower left with the clearly visible nucleus in this frame is the cell that will make all the cells of the entire gut of the adult worm. Other cells will give rise to muscle cells, nerve cells, etc. The mass of cells elongates into a worm shape (which begins around 5:32:01 in this film), and during this period some of the cells that have formed are becoming functional muscle cells, so the embryo starts to twitch and then crawl around inside the eggshell (starts around 7:24:01). In the final frame, the head is near the top, and the tail is near the bottom.
Credit: Robert P. Goldstein, UNC Chapel Hill

Sea Slugs Video

17-18-SeaSlugVideo-B

17-18-SeaSlugVideo-S

Nudibranchs, or sea slugs, belong to the phylum Mollusca, which also includes bivalves and snails. In fact, they are members of Gastropoda, the class including snails, although they have lost their shell over evolutionary time. The name nudibranch means "naked gills." You can see the gills—they are the branched structures sticking up on the back surface of the five different nudibranchs in this clip, filmed in Lembeh Straight in Indonesia. As you can see, nudibranchs are often very brightly colored and ornately patterned.
Credit: National Geographic

Lobster Mouth Parts Close Up Video

17-21-LobMthVideo-B

17-21-LobMthVideo-S

On each of the 14 fused segments of the lobster's cephalothorax there is a pair of highly specialized appendages. The first three segments bear the eyes, the antennules, and the antennae respectively. The next six segments bear the mouth parts. The video shows how the coordinated use of the feeding appendages can grip and move food to the jaws where it is crushed and swallowed. The mandibles (jaws) are borne on segment number four. These whitish plates move back and forth to cut and grind the food

before it is ingested. The next five appendages are called the first maxilla, second maxilla, first maxilliped, second maxilliped, and third maxilliped. The first and second maxillae and the first maxilliped are flattened chitinous plates that sweep the food back to the mandibles. The second and third maxillipeds are longer, leg-like appendages that can grip food and tear it apart into smaller pieces. The lobster in the video has lost one of its third maxillipeds, but a new one is being regenerated. The whole feeding mechanism is quite rapid and the final scene is shown at half speed. Note: when this lobster was caught it lacked both of its large claws. If you look carefully, you can see the pinkish stubs where new claws are being regenerated.
Credit: Courtesy of Graham R. Kent and Rebecca L. Turner, Smith College

Butterfly Emerging Video

17-26-ButflyVideo-B
17-26-ButflyVideo-S
Shown here is a time-lapse movie of the metamorphosis of a caterpillar into a Monarch butterfly. The caterpillar is the feeding larval stage, and spends its time eating and growing, molting as it grows. After it molts several times, it forms a cocoon within which it is encased as a pupa. Pockets of cells in the pupa, which had been inactive prior to this time, now begin dividing and differentiating into adult structures, while the larval structures and tissues are broken down. The most obvious adult structures are the wings, with their distinctive pattern, which can be seen through the increasingly transparent cocoon. Finally, the adult emerges, and fluid is pumped into the veins, allowing them to support the wings. The adult flies away to carry out the functions for which it is specialized: dispersal and reproduction. The adult stage derives much of its nourishment from the calories eaten and stored by the feeding larval stage. The evolution of life cycles like this, with very different stages specialized for different functions, is intriguing. Many species of butterflies also undergo extensive migrations during their life cycles.
Credit: National Geographic

Echinoderm Tube Feet Video

17-27-EchTbFtVideo-B
17-27-EchTbFtVideo-S
The sea star is a member of the phylum Echinodermata. Animals in this phylum have a distinctive mechanism of locomotion. Within the sea star is an internal water vascular system that terminates in branches called tube feet. By means of hydraulic pressure, the tube feet can be extended and, with the help of muscles at the end of the tube feet, the tube feet can form suction discs for attaching and releasing the tube feet to the substrate. Water enters the water vascular system via the madreporite which is a strainer-like structure on the dorsal side of the animal. This video shows what happens when a sea star is placed on its back in an aquarium. The tip of the sea star's arm can bend back on itself and once the tube feet engage the substrate the animal slowly pulls itself onto its correct side.
Credit: Courtesy of Graham R. Kent and Rebecca L. Turner, Smith College

Manta Ray Video

17-32A-MantaVideo-B
17-32A-MantaVideo-S
The manta ray shown here is swimming near the shallow bottom in a region of the Caribbean Sea. Rays are cartilaginous fishes which are closely related to sharks, belonging to the class Chondrichthyes. The pectoral fins of rays are greatly enlarged, and allow them to glide smoothly through the water. As is true of most rays, this manta ray is a bottom dweller that feeds on mollusks and crustaceans, after crushing them with their jaws.
Credit: National Geographic

Flapping Geese Video

16-38-FlpGeesVideo-B
16-38-FlpGeesVideo-S
The geese in this footage were filmed in Chesapeake Bay, Maryland. Geese are water birds, having higher amounts of oil on their feathers than other birds. They are strong fliers and migrate many hundreds of miles when the seasons change.
Credit: National Geographic

Soaring Hawk Video

16-38-HawkVideo-B
16-38-HawkVideo-S
The hawk in this video clip was filmed in the Galápagos Islands, soaring through the air in search of prey. The wing clearly functions as an efficient airfoil in that the leading edge is thicker than the trailing edge, its upper surface is slightly convex, and its under surface is flattened or concave. Since the air passing over the top travels further than the air passing under the wing, the air molecules are further apart thus less dense on top of the wing than underneath. This results in greater air pressure under the wing, which serves to lift the wing. Birds' bones are hollow, and they are relatively light, allowing them to reach great speeds of flight. Some birds can fly up to 170 km (about 100 miles) an hour.
Credit: National Geographic

Swans Taking Flight Video

16-38-SwanFltVideo-B
16-38-SwanFltVideo-S
These tundra swans were filmed in an Alaskan wetland. They appear very graceful while gliding through the water, but more ungainly as they take flight. Because they have relatively larger bodies than other birds, it takes several beatings of their large wings for these birds to become airborne. The sound of the wings beating resembles that of someone shaking out a tablecloth quite vigorously.
Credit: National Geographic

Bat Licking Nectar Video

17-38-BatLicVideo-B

17-38-BatLicVideo-S

Shown in this clip is a lesser long-nosed bat, *Leptonycteris mexicana*, eating sugar water from an eye dropper held by a scientist studying these interesting mammals. This bat was caught at a night roost in southeastern Arizona, where this species is quite common. *Leptonycteris mexicana* is a very social species often roosting in colonies of up to several thousand bats. They pollinate flowers of Palmer's agave (*Agave palmeri*), their only local food.

Credit: Katharine Hinman, SUNY Stony Brook, Department of Ecology and Evolution

Gibbon Swinging in a Tree Video

17-40-GibbnVideo-B

17-40-GibbnVideo-S

Gibbons are Asian apes with long arms, and are among the most acrobatic of all primates. As you can see in this clip, they swing through the trees quite gracefully and efficiently. Gibbons are the only monogamous apes. This gibbon was filmed in the rain forest in Danum Valley, Malaysia.

Credit: National Geographic

Coral Reef Fish Video

19-01-CoralRfVideo-B

19-01-CoralRfVideo-S

This footage was filmed in the Caribbean, and shows various examples of colorful fish that make up part of the incredibly diverse ecosystem of a coral reef. Some fish seen here are schools of grunts (yellow and striped yellow fish), gray snappers, and fairy basslets (the small colorful bright purple, blue, and yellow fish). You can also see sea fans (gorgonians) waving in the current.

Credit: National Geographic

Clownfish and Anemone Video

19-16-FishAneVideo-B

19-16-FishAneVideo-S

This brightly colored clownfish hovering among the tentacles of an anemone was filmed in Lembeh Straight in Indonesia. A type of symbiotic relationship has evolved between these two animals. The clownfish acts as bait and attracts predatory fish, but upon their approach the stinging tentacles of the anemone can paralyze the predator and eat it. Thus the anemone protects the clownfish from predation, and the clownfish attracts food for the anemone. This relationship is called mutualism, because the relationship is beneficial to both partners. Another interesting side-note is that the clownfish is not naturally immune to the toxin contained in the nematocysts of the anemone. Rather, the clownfish nibbles on the mucus secreted by the tentacles, and this inhibits discharge of the nematocysts by the anemone.

Credit: National Geographic

Hydrothermal Vent Video

19-40-HydtherVideo-B
19-40-HydtherVideo-S
This clip was filmed at one of the hydrothermal vents found on the bottom of the sea, approximately 2500 meters below the ocean surface. At these regions, near spreading centers of the earth's crust, molten magma is close enough to the surface of the earth to superheat the seawater. The superheated water reacts with the sulfate ion in seawater to form massive quantities of hydrogen sulfide. Some of the hydrogen sulfide reacts with metal ions within the earth's crust to form metal sulfides at very high concentrations. At the vent opening, this superheated seawater, super-enriched in metal sulfides, mixes with the cold surrounding water, causing precipitation of iron sulfide particles. The "smoke" seen in this clip is superheated water filled with iron sulfide particles.
Credit: National Geographic

Tubeworms Video

19-40-TubewrmVideo-B
19-40-TubewrmVideo-S
These large tube-dwelling worms were filmed at the Galápagos Rift in the Pacific Ocean. Some may reach more than one meter in length. Worms like these were first seen in the late 1970s, when scientists discovered an unusual assemblage of animals living on the bottom in the vicinity of hydrothermal vents. About a dozen prokaryotic species are found here which are chemoautotrophs—capable of carrying out synthesis of organic compounds using energy derived from chemical oxidation of hydrogen sulfide, rather than light. The massive amount of hydrogen sulfide formed at these regions allows these chemoautotrophic bacteria to serve as the basis for an incredibly diverse community of unusual animals, including the worms shown here. Many of these animals contain the bacteria inside themselves as symbionts that provide organic compounds as nourishment for their hosts. The vestimentiferan worms shown here were so unusual in structure that they were determined not to belong to any known phylum, and were assigned their own novel phylum.
Credit: National Geographic

Whale Eating Seal Video

22-02-WhlSealVideo-B
22-02-WhlSealVideo-S
While some whales are plankton feeders, straining small invertebrates out of the water with the comb-like plates suspended from their upper jaws (baleen), this dramatic footage shows a whale that is clearly a predator. In a split second, the killer whale is shown attacking and presumably killing a sea lion for food. Killer whales are among the largest animals on the earth.
Credit: National Geographic

T Cell Receptors Video

24-12-TCellRcVideo-S
This clip shows a T cell with fluorescently labeled (via a GFP-fusion) T cell receptor-associated molecules. The video shows the events as a T cell meets and recognizes an antigen-bearing B cell. In brief, it shows the ongoing process of molecular recognition that occurs when immune T cells detect a foreign particle in the animal. The video is a

montage of four panels (clockwise from upper left). The first shows the differential interference contrast (DIC) image, the second shows the intracellular calcium levels as determined by using a fluorescent calcium sensitive dye (calcium levels are color-coded from blue up to red), the third shows the distribution (along the cell surface) of the transmembrane T cell receptor molecule (green-red color scale), and the fourth is a three-dimensional projection of the "cap" complex at the interface of the T cell and the B cell. This latter image shows the dynamic nature of the molecular recognition event. The key molecules are eventually "corralled" into the center of the interface toward the end of the movie.
Credit: Dr. Matthew Krummel, UCSF, Department of Pathology

Rotifer Video

26-02-RotiferVideo-B
26-02-RotiferVideo-S
This clip shows a very small multicellular invertebrate called a rotifer. The Latin name for this group of animals means "wheel bearers," so named because the beating cilia in the ciliated crown, as seen in this clip, resemble a wheel rotating. Although some rotifers reach 3 mm in length, most are the size of protists, making them among the smallest metazoans. The body is surrounded by a cuticle. These animals have a complete digestive tract, and more complex inner structure than do flatworms, containing a pseudocoelom where internal organs are found.
Credit: Michael Clayton, University of Wisconsin, Madison

Sea Urchin Embryonic Development Time-Lapse Video

26-16-UrchDevVideo-B
26-16-UrchDevVideo-S
This is a series of video clips showing selected important events in sea urchin embryonic development.
1) The unfertilized egg is about 100 micrometers (μm) in diameter, similar to that of humans, and is surrounded by an extracellular layer called the vitelline layer. Upon fertilization by the first sperm, the vitelline layer becomes raised off the surface of the egg and hardens, forming the protective structure known as the fertilization membrane. All cleavages up to the blastula stage occur within this membrane.
2) During first cleavage, the nuclear envelope breaks down, and the duplicated chromosomes separate into two complete sets, followed by cytokinesis. The two new nuclei can be clearly seen. The translucent layer around the two cells, or blastomeres, is made up of hyaline protein, which surrounds and supports these early cells.
3) Second cleavage, progressing from 2 to 4 cells, is seen here. Cleavages will proceed synchronously, approximately every 30 minutes, passing through the morula stage when the cells are loosely attached to each other, up until the blastula stage.
4) The blastula stage is seen at the end of this clip. This stage is made up of a hollow ball of 1000 or so cells, arranged in a single-layered epithelium. The cells are tightly apposed to each other, maintaining a space in the center called the blastocoel cavity.
5) At the beginning of gastrulation, a number of cells in the flattened "vegetal end" at the bottom of the embryo (the vegetal plate) move as individual cells into the blastocoel cavity, where they will migrate around, fuse with each other in a ring, and begin secreting elements of the calcium carbonate skeleton of the embryo. Because these cells are the first to move as individual cells in the embryo, they are called the

primary mesenchyme cells (PMCs). The remaining cells in the vegetal plate fill in the gaps, restoring a complete epithelial sheet.

6) While the PMCs are migrating around, archenteron formation, or formation of the embryonic digestive tract, begins. The first stage involves the pushing in of the vegetal plate to form a short wide blind-ended tube.

7) This tube then narrows and elongates by a process that includes extensive cell rearrangement. Following this elongation, a subset of cells (secondary mesenchyme cells) at the tip of the archenteron will extend processes that contact a specific site on the inside of the ectodermal wall and tow the archenteron toward that spot. The wall of the ectoderm will bend inward and fuse with the tip of the archenteron to form the mouth. The digestive tract will differentiate into an esophagus, a stomach and an intestine, and the embryo will begin to feed. Four to 8 or 12 arms will extend, supported by internal skeletal elements. This feeding larva will float around in the plankton, eating algal cells, for 5 or 6 weeks, then will metamorphose into the adult form of the sea urchin.

Credit: Rachel Fink, editor, "A Dozen Eggs," Society for Developmental Biology

Frog Embryonic Development Video

26-16-FrogDevVideo-S

It is easy to observe the development of a frog embryo in pond water, and many of the developmental processes seen in a frog are also observed in other vertebrates. This time-lapse video shows the end of gastrulation and the beginning of organogenesis— particularly the beginnings of the nervous system—in *Xenopus,* the African clawed frog, an animal that is a favorite of embyrologists. The video begins with the frog embryo late in gastrulation. Cleavage has produced numerous cells too small to be seen individually. The cells roll over the lip of the blastopore and into the interior of the gastrula. Inside, lighter-colored yolk-laden cells that originated at the vegetal pole form the endoderm of the rudimentary digestive tract. Cells from the animal pole spread over the embryo and form ectoderm. In between, a layer of mesoderm is taking shape. At about 9 seconds, we are seeing the back of the embryo, with what will become the head at the top. The blastopore later becomes the anus. Under the dorsal surface, from head to tail, a rod of mesoderm called the notochord is forming; later it will be replaced by the vertebral column. Above the notochord, the ectoderm thickens, forming a neural plate, bounded by two neural folds. This is the beginning of neurulation, the formation of the nervous system. The neural folds join at the midline and the middle portion of the neural plate sinks beneath the surface, forming a neural tube. The enlarged anterior portion of the neural tube will become the frog's brain, and the posterior portion will develop into the spinal cord.

Credit: Ray Keller and John Shih, University of California, Berkeley, sponsored by the Society for Developmental Biology

Root Growth in a Radish Seed Time-Lapse Video

28-03-RootTimVideo-B

28-03-RootTimVideo-S

Roots grow not only by cell division, but also by the elongation of existing cells. Most cell division takes place in the tip of the root in a region called the apical meristem and in the tissues directly behind the meristem. Following cell division, some of the daughter cells remain as part of the meristem, but the cells 2–4 mm behind the growing tip

undergo extensive elongation in the region called the zone of elongation. Elongating cells force the root to grow down through the soil. Water is absorbed mostly by the root hairs which develop in the zone of maturation. The root hairs are small, delicate extensions of the epidermal cells that greatly increase the surface area.
Credit: Courtesy of Graham R. Kent and Rebecca L. Turner, Smith College

Sun Dew Trapping Prey Video

29-02-SunDTrpVideo-B
29-02-SunDTrpVideo-S

Some plants that live in habitats that are nutritionally poor, especially in nitrogen, have become specialized to be able to supplement their diet by occasionally catching and killing insects. This sun dew plant lives in Okefenokee Swamp in Florida. This video clip shows the function of its highly developed insect trap. Protrusions coated with sticky digestive juices must appear attractive to the insect larva inching its way up the stem. When the larva attempts to eat the glistening drops, it is swiftly caught by many other sticky protrusions, and finally the plant closes down on the larva and digests it. This movement is very rapid, and represents a response in which cells in the outer region of each lobe accumulate water and enlarge. This changes the shape of the two lobes, bringing their edges together.
Credit: National Geographic

Phototropism Video

29-14-PhototroVideo-B
29-14-PhototroVideo-S

Plants exhibit phototropism when their shoots grow towards a light source. This phenomenon is shown in the first part of the video where a Mung bean seedling, *Vigna radiata,* grows towards the lamp located in the top left side of the screen (growth has been sped up 1,800 times). Experiments have shown that plants are only responding to wavelengths of light in the blue end of the spectrum. This is illustrated in the second half of the video where another Mung bean seedling is placed between light sources: red light from the right and blue light from the left. Notice the plant eventually curves over to the left side.
Credit: Courtesy of Graham R. Kent and Rebecca L. Turner, Smith College

Gravitropism Video

29-19B-GravitVideo-B
29-19B-GravitVideo-S

Gravitropism is the response of roots and shoots to gravity. In this demonstration of gravitropism a young seedling of Mung bean (*Vigna radiata*) is rotated 90° on its side. The rate of growth is shown sped up 1,300 times. The stem quickly begins to bend and is said to exhibit negative gravitropism. Since plants also respond to light (phototropism), the light source for photosynthesis was placed below the plant to demonstrate the strong influence that the Earth's gravity has on the direction of shoot growth.
Credit: Courtesy of Graham R. Kent and Rebecca L. Turner, Smith College

Mimosa Leaf Video

29-19B-MimoLfVideo-B
29-19B-MimoLfVideo-S

Mimosa has a double compound leaf. The petiole, or leaf stalk, is attached to the stem at the node and bears four pinnae that are composed of two rows of leaflets. A mechanical stimulus, such as the touch of a finger, will cause the leaflets to fold rapidly—in less than one second. The same response can be elicited with other stimuli such as rain, wind, shaking, or severe heat. Interesting research has been conducted on the propagation of the signal from the site of stimulation to other parts of the leaf. When the terminal leaflets are given a light pinch the leaflets close in sequence. In some cases, the signal from the stimulus reaches the node and causes the petiole to flop down. Eventually, the signal reaches the base of the pinna and causes the sequential closing of leaflets from the base to the tip of the pinna.
Credit: Courtesy of Graham R. Kent and Rebecca L. Turner, Smith College

Ducklings Video

18-x1-DucklngVideo-B
18-x1-DucklngVideo-S

The wood duck and her ducklings shown here were filmed in Sun Valley, Idaho. Imprinting is a learned behavior that is limited to a specific time in a young animal's life. Mother-offspring bonding between these wood ducks is a critical step in the life cycle of these animals. It is due to this phenomenon that each of the ducklings in the nest jumps down into the water to join their mother's brood, an action that does not appear to be compelling for any other reason. Once the whole brood is together, the ducklings follow the mother closely, learning all the necessary behaviors to ensure their success.
Credit: National Geographic

Chimp Cracking Nut Video

18-x2-ChmpCrkVideo-B
18-x2-ChmpCrkVideo-S

This chimpanzee was filmed in Gombe, Africa. Chimps and humans are believed to represent two branches of anthropoids that evolved from a common ancestor, and molecular evidence suggests that chimps are more closely related to humans than to other apes. This chimp is using a big piece of wood as a tool to crack open nuts for food. Chimps are known for their high intelligence among animals.
Credit: National Geographic

Chimp Agonistic Behavior Video

18-x3-ChmpAgnVideo-B
18-x3-ChmpAgnVideo-S

This chimpanzee was filmed in Gombe, Africa. He is engaged in agonistic behavior in the form of an aggressive threat display. Behavior such as this is ritualized, most likely to gain the animal access to greater resources, whether they be food, a mate, or higher standing in the group.
Credit: National Geographic

Snake Ritual Wrestling Video

18-x4-SnkWresVideo-B

18-x4-SnkWresVideo-S

These two diamondback rattlesnakes seen carrying out a wrestling ritual were filmed in the Mojave Desert in southern California. Such agonistic behavior is a symbolic activity, which has apparently evolved to settle contests over access to resources such as a mate, food, or territory. Although diamondback rattlesnakes are not usually territorial, during the mating season they become more so. They must pass through each other's territory to gain access to females, which involves this ritual wrestling behavior.

Credit: National Geographic

Wolves Agonistic Behavior Video

18-x5-WolfAgnVideo-B

18-x5-WolfAgnVideo-S

The wolves in this clip are showing obvious agonistic behavior, in a ritual display which has probably evolved to decide which among the male wolves gains access to a resource such as a mate or food. This is generally symbolic activity, which will not result in actual injury. In this clip, you can see the wolves showing aggression by baring their teeth; erecting their ears, tail, and fur; standing upright; and looking directly at their opponent. These movements serve to make the animal appear larger and more threatening.

Credit: National Geographic

Albatross Courtship Video

18-x6-AlbaCrtVideo-B

18-x6-AlbaCrtVideo-S

These Waved Albatrosses *Diomedea (Leptorhynchus) irrorata,* are shown during their courtship ritual. Notice the behaviors: sky-pointing (head held back), beak clacking, and heads bobbing left and right. The Waved Albatross is one of the largest birds in the Galápagos. Most of the entire world population of the Waved Albatross nests on Espanola Island and is considered endemic to this Galápagos island. Albatrosses pair for life (up to forty or fifty years in some cases.) The complex courtship dance can take a very long time to complete with very ritualistic movements. These birds land on Espanola Island in late March and leave before January to wander over an extensive range along the South American coast from Ecuador to Peru.

Credit: Richard Benz, Wyckliffe School

Blue-Footed Boobies Video

18-x7-BobiCrtVideo-B

18-x7-BobiCrtVideo-S

These are Blue-Footed Boobies filmed during their courtship ritual. The Galápagos Blue-Footed Booby, *Sula nebouxi,* is the most commonly seen booby in the archipelago. It nests near the coast of most of the islands and feeds close to shore. You can see the birds displaying their blue feet to each other and notice the way they hold their wings back; this is called sky-pointing. Although both male and female are approximately the same size, their vocalizations and their eyes can distinguish the sexes. The female voice is a definite honk while the male whistles during courtship. The female eye has a

noticeably larger pupil. The male bird in this sequence is the one getting the female's attention with a definite sky-pointing behavior.
Credit: Richard Benz, Wyckliffe School

Giraffe Courtship Video

18-x8-GirfCrtVideo-B
18-x8-GirfCrtVideo-S
The two giraffes in this clip were filmed on the Serengeti Plain in Africa. They are bumping each other's necks in a courtship ritual. Courtship usually involves a complex set of behaviors believed to serve as confirmation that the participants are of the same species but of opposite sex, are in good physiological condition, and do not threaten each other.
Credit: National Geographic

Appendix C: Photo Captions

Figure 1.0a	Fungi
Figure 1.0b	DNA molecule
Figure 1.0c	Puffer fish
Figure 1.0d	Eukaryotic cell
Figure 1.1	A small sample of biology in the news
Figure 1.2	Zooming in on life
Figure 1.6	DNA technology in the drug industry
Figure 1.7	A small sample of biological diversity
Figure 1.8	The three domains of life
Figure 1.10	Digging into the past
Figure 1.12	Charles Darwin (1809–1882)
Figure 1.12x	*Origin of Species* frontispiece
Figure 1.15	Examples of artificial selection
Figure 1.16	Natural selection in action
Figure 1.17	Careful observation and measurement provide the raw data for science
Figure 1.20	Mimicry in snakes
Figure 1.22	Science as a social process
Figure 1.23	DNA technology and the law
Figure 2.0a	Vinegar bottle
Figure 2.0b	Weighing someone
Figure 2.0c	Water Strider
Figure 2.0d	Vitamin supplement
Figure 2.3x	Compound, sodium + chlorine $\rightarrow$ salt
Figure 2.4	Why is salt "iodized"?
Figure 2.6	PET scan, a medical application of radioactivity
Figure 2.7bx	Salt (sodium chloride) crystals
Figure 2.8x	Methane, ball and stick model
Figure 2.10	A watery world
Figure 2.10x	Earth, clouds and oceans
Figure 2.10x	Water, collage of photos of water in three different states
Figure 2.12	Cohesion and water transport in plants
Figure 2.12x	Trees cohesion of water
Figure 2.13	A water strider walking on water
Figure 2.13x1	Ice fishing, an example of a frozen surface with life beneath
Figure 2.13x2	Frozen water floats (left) and frozen benzene sinks (right)
Figure 2.13x3	Ice, molecular model
Figure 2.13x4	Water, molecular model

Figure 5.0a	Athlete
Figure 5.0b	Peanuts
Figure 5.0c	Overheated car
Figure 5.0d	Pizza
Figure 5.1	Regular versus stonewashed jeans
Figure 5.2	Energy conversions while snowboarding
Figure 5.2x1	Kinetic energy, child on slide
Figure 5.2x2	Potential and kinetic energy, cheetah
Figure 5.2x3	Potential and kinetic energy, dam
Figure 5.5Ax	ATP, molecular model
Figure 5.14	Plant turgor
Figure 5.17	Phagocytosis
Figure 6.0a	Pizza
Figure 6.0b	Car exhaust
Figure 6.0c	Wheat
Figure 6.0d	Exhaustion
Figure 6.1	Hitting the wall
Figure 6.2	Producer and consumer
Figure 6.16	Using fermentation to make food
Figure 6.16x	Yeast
Figure 7.1	One-year-old willow shrubs growing in an "energy plantation" in central New York
Figure 7.2	Photosynthetic autotrophs: producers for most ecosystems
Figure 7.3x1	Leaf cross section
Figure 7.3x2	Stomata, open and closed
Figure 7.6x	Chlorophyll, space-filling model
Figure 7.7	Photosynthetic pigments
Figure 7.16	An old-growth forest in the Pacific Northwest
Figure 8.0a	Galaxy
Figure 8.0b	Cytokinesis
Figure 8.0c	Chromosomes
Figure 8.0d	Sperm
Figure 8.1	A human embryo at the eight-cell stage, the result of in vitro fertilization
Figure 8.1x	Sea urchin development
Figure 8.2	Asexual reproduction
Figure 8.3	A plant cell just before division
Figure 8.3x	*E. coli* dividing
Figure 8.6x	Cell cycle collage
Figure 8.7x1	Mitosis collage, light micrographs

Figure 8.7x1a	Interphase
Figure 8.7x1b	Early prophase
Figure 8.7x1c	Late prophase
Figure 8.7x1d	Metaphase
Figure 8.7x1e	Anaphase
Figure 8.7x1f	Late telophase
Figure 8.7x2	Mitotic spindle
Figure 8.9x	Fibroblast growth
Figure 8.9x1	Breast cancer cell
Figure 8.9x2	Mammograms
Figure 8.9x2a	Mammogram (normal)
Figure 8.9x2b	Mammogram (cancer)
Figure 8.10	Growing cancer cells in the lab
Figure 8.11	The varied products of sexual reproduction
Figure 8.19	Trisomy 21 and Down syndrome
Figure 8.19x1	Human female bands
Figure 8.19x2	Human female karyotype
Figure 8.19x3	Human male bands
Figure 8.19x4	Human male karyotype
Figure 8.19x5	Down syndrome karyotype (black and white)
Figure 8.23ax	Klinefelter's karyotype
Figure 8.23bx	Translocation
Figure 8.24	Chock full of chromosomes-a tetraploid mammal?

The Process of Science Onion Tip Root

Figure 9.0a	Mendel
Figure 9.0b	Fly Malaria
Figure 9.0c	Normal Karyotype
Figure 9.0d	Queen Victoria
Figure 9.1	Amniocentesis
Figure 9.2	Heritable variation in budgies
Figure 9.4x	Gregor Mendel
Figure 9.12x	Purple and white sweet pea flowers
Figure 9.14	Examples of inherited traits in humans
Figure 9.17	Achondroplasia, a dominant trait
Figure 9.18x1	Incomplete dominance in carnations: red, pink, white
Figure 9.18x2	Red carnation
Figure 9.18x3	Pink carnation
Figure 9.18x4	White carnation
Figure 9.20x	ABO blood groups
Figure 9.21x1	Normal and sickle red blood cells
Figure 9.21x1a	Normal red blood cells

Appendix D: Art and Table Captions

Summary of Key Concepts: DNA and RNA: Polymers of Nucleotides
Summary of Key Concepts: DNA Replication
Summary of Key Concepts: Translation: The Players

Appendix E: Photo Credits

Unit openers: Unit I David Becker/Stone **Unit II** Stone **Unit III** Tom & Pat Leeson/PhotoResearchers, Inc. **Unit IV** Kennan Ward/CORBIS **Unit V** Digital Vision **Unit VI** Michael Pohuski/FoodPix

Chapter 1: Chapter opening photos top left H. Reinhard/The National Audubon Society Collection/Photo Researchers, Inc.; **top right** Dave King/Dorling Kindersley; **bottom left** N.L. Max, University of California/BPS; **bottom right** Brian Eyden/Science Photo Library/Photo Researchers, Inc. **1.1 top to bottom** U.S. News & World Report Inc.; The New York Times Co. Reprinted by permission; Knight Ridder; The New York Times Co.; TimePix; National Georgaphic Society; U.S. News & World Report Inc. **1.2 counterclockwise from top** Tom Van Sant/Geosphere Project, Santa Monica/Science Source/Photo Researchers, Inc.; CNES/Spot Image Corporation/Science Source/Photo Researchers, Inc.; Roger Wilmshurst; Frank Lane Picgure Agency/CORBIS; Science Pictures Limited/CORBIS; N.L. Max, University of California/BPS **1.6** Hank Morgan/Photo Researchers, Inc. **1.7** Charles H. Phillips **1.8 top left** Oliver Meckes/Nicole Ottawa/Photo Researchers, Inc.; **top right** K. O. Stetter, R. Huber, and R. Rachel, University of Regensburg; **middle left** D. P. Wilson/Photo Researchers, Inc.; **middle right and bottom left and right** CORBIS **1.9 left** Manfred Kage/Peter Arnold, Inc.; **middle** W. L. Dentler, University of Kansas/BPS; **right** David M. Phillips/Visuals Unlimited **1.10** Mike Hettwer **1.12 left** Richard Milner; **right** Dept. of Library Services, American Museum of Natural History **1.15a left** Anne Dowie; **right** Inga Spence/Tom Stack & Assoc. **1.15b** Chris Colling/CORBIS **1.16 left** S. Lowry/Univ. Ulster/Stone; **right** Simon Fraser/Photo Researchers, Inc. **1.17** Mary DeChirico **1.20a** Breck P. Kent **1.20b** E. R. Degginger/Photo Researchers, Inc. **1.22** NYU/Strongin **1.23** Stone

Chapter 2: Chapter opening photos top left Anne Dowie; **top right** Dorling Kindersley; **bottom left** Michael Newman/PhotoEdit; **bottom right** PLG Photo Studio **2.1 top** Photo Disc; **middle** CORBIS; **bottom** Benjamin Cummings **2.4a** Alison Wright/CORBIS **2.4b** Anne Dowie **2.6a** CTI, Inc. **2.6b** M.E. Raichle, Washington University School of Medicine **2.10** NASA **2.12 top** Alan Pappe/PhotoDisc; **bottom** R. Kessel-Shih/Visuals Unlimited **2.13** Dorling Kindersley **2.14** Harry How/Allsport (USA), Inc. **2.18** Oliver Strewe/Stone **2.19** Jagga Gudlaugnd

Chapter 3: Chapter opening photos top left Cary Groner; **top right** Alan Pappe/PhotoDisc; **bottom left** Benjamin Cummings; **bottom right** Juhn Giustina/PhotoDisc **3.1 left** PLG Photo Studio; **right** Donna Day/Stone **3.4** Anne Dowie **3.8** Scott Camazine/Photo Researchers, Inc. **3.12** Anne Dowie **3.13a and c** Biophoto Associates/Photo Researchers, Inc. **3.13b** L. M. Beidler, Florida State University **3.14 left** Jeremy Woodhouse/PhotoDisc; **right** T. J. Beveridge/Visuals Unlimited **3.17** Mike Neveux **3.18a** PhotoDisc **3.18b** Ian O'Leary/Dorling Kindersley **3.18c** William Sallaz/Duomo/CORBIS **3.18d** R. M. Motta & S. Correr/Science Source/Photo Researchers, Inc. **3.22** Stanley Flegler/Visuals Unlimited

Chapter 4: Chapter opening photos top left Anne Dowie; **top right** Tony Brain & David Parker/Science Photo Library/Photo Researchers, Inc.; **bottom left** R. M. Motta & S. Correr/Science Source/Photo Researchers, Inc.; **bottom right** Fred Felleman/Stone **4.1 left** Michael Newman/PhotoEdit; **right** Ron Boardman; Frank Lane picture Agency/CORBIS **4.2a** Victor Eroschenko **4.2b** Ars Natura **4.2c** David M. Phillips/Visuals Unlimited **4.4** CNRI/Science Photo Library/Photo Researchers, Inc. **4.11** Barry King/Biological Photo Service **4.13** Garry Cole/Biological Photo Service **4.15a** Roland Birke/Peter Arnold, Inc. **4.15b** Dr. Henry C. Aldrich/Visuals Unlimited **4.17** W. P. Wergin and E. H. Newcomb, University of Wisconsin/Biological Photo Service **4.18** Daniel S. Friend, Harvard Medical School **4.19a** M. Schliwa/Visuals Unlimited **4.19b** M. Abbey/Visuals Unlimited **4.20a** Dennis Kunkel/Phototake **4.20b** Karl Aufderheide/Visuals Unlimited **4.20c** Science Photo Library/Photo Researchers, Inc. **4.23** Peter B. Armstrong, University of California, Davis

Chapter 5: Chapter opening photos top left Susanna Price/Dorling Kindersley; **top right** Paul Barton/CORBIS; **bottom left** William Sallaz/Duomo/CORBIS; **bottom right** C Squared Studios **5.1** Greg Kuchik/Getty Images, Inc. **5.2** Russell Chun and Maureen Kennedy **5.14** Nigel Cattlin/Holt Studios International/Photo Researchers, Inc. **5.17** Mike Abbey/Visuals Unlimited **5.19** Eyewire

Chapter 6: Chapter opening photos top left CORBIS; **top right** Eyewire; **bottom left** Steve Allen/The Image Bank; **bottom right** Clive Brunskill/Getty Images **6.1** Ted Spiegel/CORBIS **6.2** Gail Shumway/

Taxi **6.4** CORBIS **6.16a** Steve Welsh/Liaison Agency, Inc. **6.16b** Ian O'Leary/Dorling Kindersley

Chapter 7: Chapter opening photos top left Craig Tuttle/CORBIS; **top right** Digital Vision; **bottom left** Marge Lawson **7.1** Tim Volk **7.2a** Renee Lynn/Photo Researchers, Inc. **7.2b** Bob Evans/Peter Arnold, Inc. **7.2c** Dwight Kuhn **7.2d** Sue Barns **7.3 top** M. Eichelberger/Visuals Unlimited; **bottom** W.P. Wergin and E.H. Newcomb, University of Wisconsin/Biological Photo Service **7.6** Adam Smith/Taxi **7.7** Siegfried Layda/Stone **7.8b** Christine L. Case **7.8c** Tony Freeman/PhotoEdit **7.14a** C.F. Miescke/Biological Photo Service **7.14b** Stone **7.16** Tom and Pat Leeson

Chapter 8: Chapter opening photos top left Luke Dodd/Science Source/Photo Researchers, Inc.; **top right** David M. Phillips/Science Source/Photo Researchers, Inc.; **bottom left** David M. Phillips/Science Source/Photo Researchers, Inc.; **bottom right** Dennis Kunkel/Phototake **8.1** Phototake NYC **8.2a** Biophoto Associates/Photo Researchers, Inc. **8.2b** Brian Parker/Tom Stack & Associates, Inc. **8.3** Andrew Bajer/University of Oregon **8.4 top** A.L. Olins, Univ. of Tennessee/Biological Photo Service; **bottom** Biophoto Associates/Photo Researchers, Inc. **8.7 all** Conly Rieder **8.8a** David M. Phillips/Visuals Unlimited **8.8b** Carolina Biological Supply/Phototake NYC **8.10** James King-Holmes/Science Source/Photo Researchers, Inc. **8.11** Gary Buss/Taxi **8.12** CNRI/SPL/Photo Researchers, Inc. **8.19 left** CNRI/Science Photo Library/Photo Researchers, Inc.; **right** Greenlar/The Image Works **8.24** Dr. Martin Gallardo, Universidad Austral de Chile **Page 140** Carolina Biological Supply/Phototake NYC

Chapter 9: Chapter opening photos top left CORBIS Bettmann; **top right** PhotoDisc; **bottom left** Sinclair Stammers/Science Photo Library/Photo Researchers, Inc.; **bottom right** AKG London Ltd **9.1** Yoav Levy/Phototake NYC **9.2** Hans Reinhard/Bruce Coleman Photography **9.4** CORBIS Bettmann **9.14 top left** CORBIS; **top right** Eyewire; **middle left and right** PhotoDisc; **bottom left and right** Anthony Loveday **9.17** Dick Zimmerman/Shooting Star International Photo Agency **9.21** Lawrence Berkeley National Laboratory **9.28a** Jean Claude Revy/Phototake NYC **9.28b** Carolina Biological Supply/Phototake NYC **9.31** Taxi **9.32** Dr. Tudor Parfitt, University of London **Page 169** Norma Jubinville

Chapter 10: Chapter opening photos top left Juda Ngwenya/REUTERS/Getty Images; **top right** Keith V. Wood, University of California, San Diego; **bottom left** Richard Wagner, UCSF Graphics; **bottom right** Alfred Pasieka/Photo Researchers, Inc. **10.3a** Barrington Brown/Photo Researchers Inc **10.3b** Cold Spring Harbor Laboratory Archives **10.5** Michael Freeman/Phototake **10.7** B. Daemmrich/The Image Works **10.12** Keith V. Wood, University of California, San Diego **10.23** A. Witte/Stone **10.24** Francis Leroy, Biocosmos/ Science Source/Photo Researchers, Inc. **10.25** Oliver Meckes/Photo Researchers **10.27** Holt Studios/Jurgen Dielenschneider/The National Audubon Society Collection/Photo Researchers, Inc. **10.30** NIBSC/Science Photo Library/Photo Researchers, Inc. **10.31a** CDC/Phototake, NYC **10.31b** Keith V. Wood/Photo Researchers, Inc. **10.32** Christian Keenan/Getty Images

Chapter 11: Chapter opening photos top left Anne Dowie; **top right** PhotoDisc; **bottom left** Geoff Brightling/Dorling Kindersley; **bottom right** Lee Snider/The Image Works **11.1 main** Craig Hammell/Stock Market/CORBIS; **inset** Courtesy of Cord Blood Registry **11.2 all** Ed Reschke **11.4b** Incyte Pharmaceuticals, Inc., Palo Alto, CA, from R. F. Service, Science (1998) 282:396–399, with permission from Science **11.6** Roslin Institute, Edinburgh **11.7a** Jim Curley/University of Missouri **11.7b** Advanced Cell Technology, Inc. **11.9** Jose Cibelli/Advanced Cell Technology **11.12** Dave King/Dorling Kindersley **11.21** Edward B.Lewis/California Institute of Technology

Chapter 12: Chapter opening photos top left both PhotoDisc; **top right** Andrew Brookes/CORBIS; **bottom left** T. J. Berveridge and S. Schultze/Biological Photo Service; **bottom right** James P. Blair/CORBIS **12.1** Douglas Graham/Roll Call/Corbis Sygma **12.3** SIU/Visuals Unlimited **12.4** Hank Morgan/Photo Researchers, Inc. **12.5a** CORBIS **12.5b** Ken Ostlie **12.6** Peter Berger, Institut fur Biologie, Freiburg **12.7** PPL Therapeutics **12.8 top** S. Cohen/Science Source/Photo Researchers, Inc.; **bottom** Huntington Potter, University of South Florida and David Dressler, Oxford University **12.14** Steve Miller/AP/Wide World Photos **12.19** Cellmark Diagnostics Inc., Germantown, Maryland **12.20** Koji Sasahara/AP Photo **12.22** Department of Energy, Joint Genome Institute. Photograph by Michael Anthony. **12.24** Alfred Wolf/Science Source/Photo Researchers, Inc. **12.25** AFP/CORBIS **12.26** University of California, San Francisco

Chapter 13: Chapter opening photos top left Lara Jo Regan/Getty Images; **top right** Leonard Lessin/Peter Arnold, Inc.; **bottom right** Larry Burrows, TimePix **13.1** CORBIS **13.2a** E. S. Ross, California Academy of Sciences **13.2b** Ken G. Preston-Mafham/

Animals Animals **13.2c** P. and W. Ward/Animals Animals **13.3 left** Larry Burrows, Life Magazine ©Time Inc.; **right** National Maritime Museum, London **13.4** William Paton/NHPA **13.7** CORBIS **13.8** Philip Gingerich 1991. Reprinted with permission of Discover Magazine **13.9 left** Dorling Kindersley; **middle** Worldsat International and J. Knighton/ Science Source/Photo Researchers, Inc.; **right** Ken Findlay/Dorling Kindersley **13.11a** Dwight Kuhn Photography **13.11b** Lennart Nilsson/Albert Bonniers Forlag AB, A Child Is Born, Dell Publishing. 1990 **13.13a** Tui de Roy/Bruce Coleman, Inc. **13.13b** Mike Putland/Ardea London Ltd. **13.13c** Tui de Roy/Bruce Coleman, Inc. **13.14** Michael Fogden/DRK Photo **13.16a** David Cavagnaro **13.16b** USAF, NOAA/ NESDIS at Univ. of CO, CIRES/National Snow and Ice Data Center **13.17** Edmund Brodie, Indiana University **13.19** Anne Dowie **13.22** EyeWire **13.23** Hulton-Deutsch Collection/CORBIS **13.24** 1993 Time magazine **13.25** Michael Fogden/DRK Photo **13.27** Bill Longcore/Photo Researchers, Inc.

Chapter 14: chapter opening photos top left A. Witte/Stone; **top right** Auguste Rodin, Le Penseur, private collection/The BridgemanArt Library; **bottom right** George Bernard/The National Audubon Society Collection/Photo Researchers, Inc. **14.1** Mark Pilkington/Geological Survey of Canada/SPL/Photo Researchers, Inc. **14.3** Ernst Mayr, Museum of comparative Zoology, Harvard University **14.4a left** John Shaw/Tom Stack and Associates; **right** Don & Pat Valenti/Tom Stack & Associates **14.4b all** PhotoDisc **14.6** Wolfgang Kaehler/CORBIS **14.7 left** CORBIS; **middle** Karl Shone/Dorling Kindersley; **right** Eye-Wire **14.9 main photo** CORBIS; **left inset** John Shaw/Bruce Coleman, Inc.; **right inset** Michael Fogden/Bruce Coleman **14.11 all** University of Amsterdam **14.15** Chip Clark **14.16** Stephen Dalton/Photo Researchers, Inc. **14.17 both** PhotoDisc **14.18a** Georg Gerster/Science Source/Photo Researchers, Inc. **14.18b** John Reader/Science Photo Library/Photo Researchers, Inc. **14.18c** Tom Bean/CORBIS **14.18d** Manfred Kage/Peter Arnold, Inc. **14.18e** Chip Clark **14.18f** Tom Bean/CORBIS **14.18g** David A. Grimald. Photo by Jacklyn Beckett/The American Museum of Natural History, N.Y. **14.18h** F. Latreille/Cerpolex/ Cercles Polaires Expeditions **14.24** Hanny Paul/ Liaison Agency, Inc.

Chapter 15 Chapter opening photos top left P. Motta/Science Source/Photo Researchers, Inc.; **top right** David M. Frazier/Photo Researchers, Inc.; **bottom left** USDA/The National Audubon Society Collection/Photo Researchers, Inc.; **bottom right** Frederick P. Mertz/Visuals Unlimited **15.1** Alex Wong/Getty

Images **15.3** Artist: Peter Sawyer ©NMNH Smithsonian Inst. **15.4** Roger Ressmeyer/Corbis **15.7a** Sidney Fox, University of Miami/BPS **15.7b** F. M. Menger and Kurt Gabrielson, Emory University **15.8a** Stanley Awramik/Biological Photo Service **15.8b** Dr. Tony Brain and David Parker/Science Photo Library/Photo Researchers inc. **15.9** Helen E. Carr/BPS **15.10a** David M. Phillips/Visuals Unlimited **15.10b** David M. Phillips/Visuals Unlimited **15.10c** CNRI/SPL/ Photo Researchers Inc. **15.11a** David M. Phillips/ Science Source/Photo Researchers, Inc. **15.11b** Sue Barns **15.11c** Heide Schulz, Max Planck Institute for Marine Microbiology **15.12** Lee D. Simon/Science Source/Photo Researchers, Inc. **15.13** H.S. Pankratz, T.C. Beaman/Biological Photo Service **15.14** Dr. Tony Brain/Science Source/Photo Researchers, Inc. **15.15a** R. Calentine/Visuals Unlimited **15.15b** Centers for Disease Control **15.16** Martin Bond/The National Audubon Society Collection/Photo Researchers, Inc. **15.17** Exxon Corporation **15.19a** Oliver Meckes/Science Source/Photo Researchers, Inc. **15.19b** M. Abbey/Visuals Unlimited **15.19c** Manfred Kage/Peter Arnold, Inc. **15.19d** Dr. Masamichi Aikawa **15.19e** M. Abbey/Science Source/Photo Researchers, Inc. **15.20** George Barron **15.21 left** Matt Springer, Stanford University; **right top and bottom** Robert Kay, MRC Cambridge **15.22a** Biophoto Associates/Photo Researchers, Inc. **15.22b** Kent Wood/ Photo Researchers, Inc. **15.22c** Herb Charles Ohlmeyer, Fran Heyl Associates **15.22d** Manfred Kage/Peter Arnold **15.23a** A. Flowers and L. Newman/Photo Researchers, Inc. **15.23b** Gary Robinson/Visuals Unlimited **15.23c** David Hall/Photo Researchers, Inc.

Chapter 16: Chapter opening photos top left Sequoia National Park Service; **top right** Anne Dowie; **bottom left** CORBIS; **bottom right** G. Prance/Visuals Unlimited **16.1** Lara Hartley **16.3** Dana Richter/ Visuals Unlimited **16.4** David Middleton/NHPA **16.5** Graham Kent **16.6a** E.R. Degginger/Science Source/Photo Researchers, Inc. **16.6b** Linda.E. Graham **16.8** J. Shaw, Biology Department, Duke University **16.9** Dwight Kuhn/Dwight Kuhn Photography **16.11 left inset** Milton Rand/Tom Stack and Associates; **main photo** John Shaw/Tom Stack & Associates; **bottom inset** Glenn Oliver/Visuals Unlimited **16.12** TheField Museum, Chicago **16.13** Ron Watts/CORBIS **16.15 left inset** Derrick Ditchburn/ Visuals Unlimited; **main photo** Doug Sokell/Visuals Unlimited; **right inset** Gerald & Buff Corsi/Visuals Unlimited **16.19a** Taxi **16.19b** Scott Camazine/Photo Researchers, Inc. **16.19c** Dwight R. Kuhn **16.20a** H. Reinhard/The National Audubon Society Collection/Photo Researchers, Inc. **16.20b** Rob Simpson/

Visuals Unlimited **16.20c** G. L. Barron, University of Guelph/Biological Photo Service **16.20d left** M. F. Brown/Visuals Unlimited; **right** Jack Bostrack/Visuals Unlimited **16.20e** N. Allin and G. L. Barron, University of Guelph/Biological Photo Service **16.20f** J. Forsdyke/Gene Cox/Science Source/Photo Researchers, Inc. **16.21** Fred Rhoades/Mycena Consulting **16.22a** Stuart Bebb/Oxford Scientific Films/Animals Animals/Earth Scenes **16.22b** David Cavagnaro/Visuals Unlimited **16.23a** Robb Walsh **16.23b** PhotoDisc **16.24** Christine Case **16.25 top** Dr. Jeremy Burgess/The National Audubon Society Collection/Photo Researchers, Inc.; **bottom** V. Ahmadijian/Visuals Unlimited

Chapter 17: Chapter opening photos top left Steve P. Hopkin/Taxi; **top right** Francois Gohier/The National Audubon Society Collection/Photo Researchers, Inc.; **bottom left** R. Calentine/Visuals Unlimited; **bottom right** Jeremy Woodhouse/Getty Images, Inc. **17.1a and b** David Hosking/CORBIS **17.2** Gunter Ziesler/Peter Arnold, Inc. **17.3** Anthony Mercieca/Photo Researchers, Inc. **17.9** Photodisc Green **17.11a** CORBIS **17.11b** Claudia Mills/Friday Harbor Labs **17.12** Mike Bacon/Tom Stack & Associates, Inc. **17.15** Stanley Fleger/Visuals Unlimited **17.16a** Reprinted with permission from A. Eizinger and R. Sommer, Max Planck Institut fur Entwicklungsbiologie, Tubingen. Copyright 2000 American Association for the Advancement of Science **17.16b** Andrew Syred/Science Photo Library/Photo Researchers **17.18a** Tony Craddock/The National Audubon Society Collection/Photo Researchers, Inc. **17.18b** H.W. Pratt/BPS **17.18c** Charles R. Wyttenbach/Biological Photo Service **17.20a** A.N.T./NHPA **17.20b left** R. DeGoursey/Visuals Unlimited; **right** CORBIS **17.20c** Astrid & Hanns-Frieder Michler/Science Source/Photo Researchers, Inc. **17.22a** William Dow/CORBIS **17.22b** D. Suzio/Photo Researchers, Inc. **17.22c** Oliver Meckes/Photo Researchers, Inc. **17.23a** CORBIS **17.23b** A. Kerstitch/Visuals Unlimited **17.24** Carolina Biological Supply Company/Phototake NYC **17.26a–e** John Shaw/Tom Stack and Associates **17.27a left** Gerald Corsi/Visuals Unlimited; **right** Gary Milburn/Tom Stack **17.27b** David Wrobel **17.27c** Fred Bavendam/Peter Arnold, Inc. **17.28** Biophoto Associates/Photo Researchers Inc. **17.29a** Runk/Schoenberger/Grant Heilman Photography, Inc. **17.29b** Robert Brons/Biological Photo Service **17.32a** George Grall/National Geographic Image Collection **17.32b** J. M. Labat/Jacana/Photo Researchers Inc. **17.33a** Geoff Brightling/Dorling Kindersley **17.33b** Hans Pfletschinger/Peter Arnold Inc. **17.33c** Dr. Eckart Pott/Bruce ColemanLtd. **17.35** Robert and Linda Mitchell

17.36 The Natural History Museum, London **17.37** Stephen J. Kraseman/DRK Photo **17.38a** Mervyn Griffiths/CSIRO **17.38b** Dan Hadden/Ardea London Ltd **17.38c** Mitch Reardon/The National Audubon Society Collection/Photo Researchers, Inc. **17.39** Digital Vision **17.40a** E. H. Rao/Photo Researchers, Inc. **17.40b** Kevin Schafer/Photo Researchers, Inc. **17.40c** Digital Vision **17.40d** Digital Vision **17.40e** Digital Vision **17.40f** Nancy Adams/Tom Stack and Assoc. **17.40g** Digital Vision **17.40h** Karl Weatherly/Getty Images, Inc. **17.43a** Cleveland Museum of Natural History **17.43b** John Reader/SPL/Photo Researchers, Inc. **17.43c** Institute of Human Origins, photo by Donald Johanson **17.45 all** Jean Clottes/Corbis/Sygma

Chapter 18: Chapter opening photos top left Pete Seaward/Stone; **top right** John D. Cunningham/Visuals Unlimited; **bottom left** Raymond Gehman/CORBIS; **bottom right** S. P. Gillette/CORBIS **18.1** Joel W. Rogers/CORBIS **18.2a and b** Raphael Gaillarde/Liaison Agency, Inc. **18.3** Reprinted with permission from D.W. Schindler, Science 184 (1974): 897, Figure 1.49. 1974 American Association for the Advancement of Science **18.4a** Francois Gohier/The National Audubon Society Collection/Photo Researchers, Inc. **18.4b** Ingrid Van Den Berg/Animals Animals/Earth Scenes **18.4c** David Lazenby/Planet Earth Pictures **18.4d** Nigel J. Dennis/NHPA **18.5** Erich Hartmann/Magnum Photos, Inc. **18.6** Joel W. Rogers/CORBIS **18.7** Los Angeles Times. Reprinted with permission **18.8** Stephen Krasemann/Photo Researchers, Inc. **18.9** CORBIS **18.10** Brian Parker/Tom Stack & Associates, Inc. **18.11 left** Raymond Gehman/CORBIS; **right** Scott T. Smith/CORBIS **18.13** Robert Brenner/PhotoEdit **18.14** Jim Brandenburg/Minden Pictures **18.15a and b** Frans Lanting/Minden Pictures **18.16a** Sophie de Wilde/Jacana/Photo Researchers, Inc. **18.16b** Art Wolfe/The Image Bank **18.16c** Will & Deni McIntryre/Photo Researchers, Inc. **18.17** Earth Satellite Corporation **18.19** Roy Corral/CORBIS **18.22** Runk/Schoenberger/Grant Heilman Photography, Inc. **18.23** Nigel Cattlin/The National Audubon Society Collection/Photo Researchers, Inc. **18.24** Alan Carey/Photo Researchers, Inc. **18.26** Mahaux Photography/The Image Bank **18.28a** Alain Evrard/Photo Researchers, Inc. **18.28b** Pete Seaward/Stone **18.30** Tom Bean/CORBIS **18.31** David Reznick **Table 18.2 left** CORBIS; **right** Ernest Manewa/Visuals Unlimited

Chapter 19: Chapter opening photos top left Gary W. Carter/CORBIS; **top right** Darryl Torckler/Stone; **bottom left** Lester Lefkowitz/CORBIS; **bottom right** Jeffrey L. Rotman/CORBIS **19.1** A. Witte/Stone

19.2 Richard D. Estes/Photo Researchers Inc. 19.4 Galen Rowell/Photo Researchers, Inc. 19.6 both Heather Angel/Biofotos 19.7b Joseph T. Collins/ Photo Researchers, Inc. 19.7c Kevin de Queiroz, National Museum of Natural History 19.8 Arthur Morris/©VIREO 19.9 Jeff Lepore/Photo Researchers, Inc. 19.10 Jerry Young/Dorling Kindersley 19.11 Gail Shumway/Taxi 19.12a Lincoln Brower, Sweet Briar College 19.12b Peter J. Mayne 19.13a Dr. Edward S. Ross 19.13b Runk/Schoenberger/Grant Heilman Photography, Inc. 19.14 William E. Townsend/Photo Researchers, Inc. 19.15 Australiian Embassy Photo Library 19.16 Michael Fogden/DRK Photo 19.18.1 David Muench/CORBIS 19.18.2 Tom Bean/Tom & Susan Bean, Inc. 19.18.3 Andrew Brown; Ecoscene/ CORBIS 19.18.4 Tom Bean/Tom & Susan Bean, Inc. 19.18.5 Tom Bean/Tom & Susan Bean, Inc. 19.18.6 Tom Bean/Tom & Susan Bean, Inc. 19.19 John Sohlden/Visuals Unlimited 19.22 Gregory G. Dimijian/Photo Researchers, Inc. 19.31a David Samuel Robbins/CORBIS 19.31b and c Joe McDonald/ CORBIS 19.31d Charles Mauzy/CORBIS 19.31e Jake Rajs/Stone 19.31f Kennan Ward/CORBIS 19.31g Richard Hamilton Smith/CORBIS 19.31h Darrell Gulin/CORBIS 19.32a WorldSat International/ Science Source/Photo Researchers, Inc. 19.32b Williams H. Mullins/Photo Researchers, Inc. 19.32c David Muench/CORBIS 19.34 M.E. Warren/Photo Researchers, Inc. 19.36 Frans Lanting/Photo Researchers, Inc. 19.37 main photo Emory Kristof/ National Geographic Society Image Collection; inset D. Foster/Visuals Unlimited 19.38 all Lawrence E. Gilbert/Biological Photo Service

Chapter 20: Chapter opening photos top left James P. Blair/National Geographic Image Collection; **top right** David Lazenby/Planet Earth Pictures; **bottom left** AFP/CORBIS; **bottom right** Lynda Richardson/ CORBIS 20.1a 2002 Getty Images 20.1b Rachel Woodfield, Merkel + Associates 20.2 Susan Barnett 20.3a Buddy Mays/CORBIS 20.3b Lynda Richardson/CORBIS 20.3c Marc Dantzker 20.3d main J. Lubner/Wisconsin Sea Grant; inset Scott Camazine/ The National Audubon Society Collection/Photo Researchers, Inc. 20.4 CORBIS 20.5 Nigel Tucker/ Planet Earth Pictures 20.6a John D. Cunningham/Visuals Unilimited. 20.6b Northeastern Forest Experiment Station, Forest Service, United States Department of Agriculture 20.8 NASA Earth Observing System 20.9 CORBIS 20.11 Craig Aurness/ CORBIS 20.12a NASA/Goddard Space Flight Center 20.12c Bill Bachmann/Photo Edit 20.13 Fred Bavendam/Minden Pictures 20.14a AFP/CORBIS 20.14b Mark Carwardine/Still Pictures/Peter Arnold, Inc.

20.14c Dieter & Mary Plage/Bruce Coleman Inc. 20.15a Wayne Lawler/CORBIS 20.15b Gary Kramer 20.15c Richard Vogel/Liaison Agency, Inc. 20.16 Scott Camazine/Photo Researchers, Inc. 20.17 left Charles Mauzy/CORBIS; right David Samuel Robbins/CORBIS 20.18 top Gary Braasch/Woodfin Camp & Associate; bottom Greg Vaughn/Tom Stack & Associates 20.19a Rob Curtis/The Early Birder 20.19b Raymond K. Gehman/National Geographic Society Image Collection 20.19c Blanche Haning/ The Lamplighter 20.20a David Hosking/Photo Researchers Inc. 20.20b James P. Blair/National Geographic Image Collection 20.21 Florida Department of Transportation 20.22b, 20.23 and 20.24 Frans Lanting/Minden Pictures

Chapter 21: Chapter opening photos top left Rodney Hyett; Elizabeth Whiting & Associates/CORBIS; **top right** Dr. Rodolfo Llinas/Peter Arnold, Inc.; **bottom left** K. M. Highfill/Photo Researchers, Inc.; **bottom right** Anthony Loveday 21.1 Norbert Schaefer/ CORBIS 21.3a PhotoDisc 21.3b Janice Sheldon 21.3c T. D. Parsons, D. Kleinfeld, F. Raccuia-Behling and B. Salzberg. Biophysical Journal, July 1989. Photo courtesy of Brian Salzberg. 21.10 Science Photo Library/ Photo Researchers, Inc. 21.14a Art Wolfe/The Image Bank 21.14b Leo Dennis/NewSport/Corbis 21.18 Hank Morgan/Photo Researchers, Inc. 21.19a Photodisc 21.19b Brandon D. Cole/CORBIS 21.19c CORBIS 21.19d Amos Nachoum/CORBIS 21.19e CORBIS 21.19f George Hall/CORBIS

Chapter 22: Chapter opening photos top left Ryan McVay/PhotoDisc; **top right** Eric J. Simon; **bottom left** Oliver Meckes/Photo Researchers, Inc.; **bottom right** PLG Photo Studio 22.1 Matthew Peyton/Getty Images 22.2a Tom Eisner, Cornell University 22.2b Alissa Crandall/CORBIS 22.2c Burke/Triolo Productions/Food Pix 22.11 Oliver Meckes/Photo Researchers, Inc. 22.18a both PhotoDisc 22.18b all Dorling Kindersley 22.20 Dagmar Fabricius/Stock Boston 22.22 The Jackson Laboratory 22.23 Eric J. Simon

Chapter 23: Chapter opening photos top left Science Photo Library/Photo Researchers, Inc.; **top right** NASA/Goddard Space Flight Center; **bottom left** Andrew Syred/Stone; **bottom right** Richard Hutchings/CORBIS 23.1 Bruce Ayres/Stone 23.7b Photodisc 23.9a Lennart Nilsson, The Body Victorious, Dell Publishing Company 23.12 Andrew Syred/ Stone 23.13 Gillette Research Institute 23.15a Ed Reschke 23.15b W. Ober/Visuals Unlimited 23.24a and b Martin Rotker 23.25 Zig Leszczynski/Animals Animals

Chapter 24: Chapter opening photos top left Manfred Kage/Peter Arnold, Inc.; **top right** Aaron Haupt/Photo Researchers, Inc.; **bottom left** Steve Prezant/CORBIS; **bottom right** Tom Van Sant/Photo Researchers, Inc. **24.1** NIBSC/Science Photo Library/Photo Researchers, inc. **24.3** Science Photo Library/Photo Researchers, Inc. **24.6** Photodisc Green **24.8** Aaron Haupt/Photo Researchers, Inc. **24.15** Dey, L.P. **24.17** M. English, MD/Custom Medical Stock Photo **24.18** Photodisc Green **24.19** John Cardamone, Jr., University of Pittsburgh/BPS **24.20** National Archives

Chapter 25: Chapter opening photos top left Gary Conner/PhotoEdit; **top right** HIH/Science Source/Photo Researchers, Inc.; **bottom left** AFP/CORBIS; **bottom right** Lennart Nilsson/A Child is Born, Dell Publishing **25.1** Robert Brenner/PhotoEdit **25.8a** Michael Abramson/Getty Images **25.8b** American Journal of Medicine 20:133, 1956. **25.8c** Lee Celano/AFP/CORBIS **25.9** Alison Wright/CORBIS **25.13** CORBIS

Chapter 26: Chapter opening photos top left Yorgos Nikas/Stone; **top right** Annie Griffiths Belt/CORBIS; **bottom left** Yorgos Nikas/Stone Allstock; **bottom right** C. Edelman/La Vilette/Photo Researchers, Inc. **26.1** Brooks Kraft/Sygma **26.2a** David Wrobel **26.2b** Roland Birke/OKAPIA/Photo Researchers, Inc. **26.3a** Jim Solliday/Biological Photo Service **26.3b** Robin Chittenden/CORBIS **26.3c** Dwight Kuhn **26.5** C. Edelman/La Vilette/Photo Researchers, Inc. **26.11** Charles Thatcher/Stone Allstock **26.12** Michael Tamborrino/Taxi **26.13** Yorgos Nikas/Stone **26.23–26.25** Lennart Nilsson/A Child is Born, Dell Publishing **26.26 main photo** Eric J. Simon; **inset** Stone

Chapter 27: Chapter opening photos top left Georgina Bowater/CORBIS; **top right** Digital Vision; **bottom left** Jonathan Nourok/PhotoEdit; **bottom right** Dana Boatman & John Freeman, Johns Hopkins School of Medicine **27.1** Photodisc Green **27.3** Manfred Kage/Peter Arnold, Inc. **27.14** Dana Boatman & John Freeman, Johns Hopkins School of Medicine **27.28** Reuters NewMedia Inc./CORBIS **27.30** Clara Franzini-Armstrong, University of Pennsylvania **27.34** Chris Urso/Associated Press, AP **27.35** M. Peres/Custom Medical Stock Photo

Chapter 28: Chapter opening photos top left Robert Holmes/CORBIS; **top right** Runk/Schoenberger/Grant Heilman, Inc.; **bottom left** Jeri Gleiter/Taxi; **bottom right** Michael Fogden/DRK Photo **28.1** N. Cattlin/Photo Researchers, Inc. **28.3** Dennis Kunkel Microscopy, Inc. **28.4 both** Walter Chandoha **28.6a** Peter Anderson/Dorling Kindersley **28.6b** CORBIS **28.8a** Dwight Kuhn **28.8b and c** Graham Kent **28.8d** R. Kessel-Shih/Visuals Unlimited **28.8e** Randy Moore/Visuals Unlimited **28.10 and 28.11** Ed Reschke **28.12a** Kevin Schafer **28.12b** Frank Balthis **28.12c** Galen Rowell/Mountain Light **28.18 all** W.H. Hodge/Peter Arnold, Inc. **28.19 all** PhotoDisc **28.20** Barry Runk/Grant Heilman, Inc. **28.21a** Robert Holmes/CORBIS **28.21b** Jeri Gleiter/Taxi **28.25** Runk/Schoenberger/Grant Heilman, Inc. **28.26** D. Wilder/Wilder Nature Photography

Chapter 29: Chapter opening photos top left Alan Keohane/Dorling Kindersley; **top right** Oliver Benn/Stone; **bottom left** Oliver Benn/Stone; **bottom right** Rich Iwasaki/Stone **29.1** CORBIS **29.3** Renee Lynn/Photo Researchers, Inc. **29.4** Grant Heilman/Grant Heilman, Inc. **29.5a** James Pushnik, California State University, Chico **29.5b** Holt Studios/Earth Scenes **29.5c and d** James Pushnik, California State University, Chico **29.6** Brian Capon **29.7** R. L. Peterson/Biological Photo Service **29.9a** Wally Eberhart/Visuals Unlimited **29.9b** E.H. Newcomb and S.R. Tandon/Biological Photo Service **29.12** Ray F. Evert/University of Wisconsin **29.14** M. T. Frazie/Photo Researchers, Inc. **29.16** Runk/Schoenberger/Grant Heilman, Inc. **29.17** Fred Jensen/UC Davis **29.18** Richard Cummins/CORBIS **29.19a** Scott Camazine/Photo Researchers, Inc. **29.19b** Michael Evans, Ohio State University **29.21 main photo** Michele Westmorland/The Image Bank; **inset** M.H. Zimmermann

Appendix F: Illustration and Table Credits

The following figures are adapted from Lawrence G. Mitchell, John A. Mutchmor, and Warren D. Dolphin, *Zoology* (Menlo Park, CA: Benjamin/Cummings, 1988) © 1988 The Benjamin/Cummings Publishing Company: **17.3, 17.30.**

The following figures are adapted from C. K. Mathews and K. E. van Holde, *Biochemistry* (Menlo Park, CA: Benjamin/Cummings, 1996) © 1996 The Benjamin/Cummings Publishing Company: **6.12, 8.4.**

Figure 1.21: Adapted from Neil. A. Campbell, Brad Williamson, and Robin J. Heyden, *Biology: Exploring Life* (Upper Saddle River, NJ: Prentice Hall, 2004) © 2004 Pearson Education, Inc.

Figure 4.18: Adapted from W. M. Becker, L. J. Kleinsmith, and J. Hardin, *The World of the Cell* (San Francisco, CA: Benjamin Cummings, 2000) © 2000 The Benjamin Cummings Publishing Company.

Figure 5.4: Data from C. M. Taylor and G. M. McLeod, *Rose's Laboratory Handbook for Dietetics,* 5th ed. (New York: Macmillan, 1949), p. 18; J. V. G. A. Durnin and R. Passmore, 1967, *Energy and Protein Requirements* in *FAO/WHO Technical Report* No. 522, 1973; W. D. McArdle, F. I. Katch, and V. L. Katch, 1981, *Exercise Physiology* (Philadelphia, PA: Lea & Feibiger, 1981); R. Passmore and J. V. G. A. Durnin, *Physiological Reviews* 35 (1955): 801–840; USDA, McDonald's, Kentucky Fried Chicken, http://www.cyberdiet.com.

Figure 6.6: Adapted from Alberts et al., *Molecular Biology of the Cell,* 2nd ed., fig. 7.17, p. 351 (New York: Garland Publishing, 1989). Copyright © 1989. Reproduced by permission of Taylor & Francis, Inc., http://www.taylorandfrancis.com.

Figure 7.11: From Richard and David Walker, *Energy, Plants and Man,* fig. 4.1, p. 69 (Sheffield: University of Sheffield). Copyright David and Richard Walker. Reprinted by permission.

Figure 8.23: Adapted from F. Vogel and A. G. Motulsky, *Human Genetics* (New York: Springer-Verlag, 1982). Copyright 1982 Springer-Verlag.

Figure 9.15: Adapted from *Everyone Here Spoke Sign Language* by Nora Ellen Groce. Copyright 1985 by Nora Ellen Groce. Reprinted by permission of Harvard University Press.

Figure 9.21: From *Introduction to Genetic Analysis,* 4th ed. by Suzuki, Griffiths, Miller, and Lewontin.

Copyright 1976, 1981, 1986, 1989, 1993, 1996 by W. H. Freeman and Company. Used with permission.

Chapter 10, page 192: Text quotation by Joshua Lederberg, from Barbara J. Culliton, "Emerging Viruses, Emerging Threat," *Science,* vol. 247, p. 279 (19 January 1990). Copyright © 1990 American Association for the Advancement of Science.

Table 11.1: Data from the the American Cancer Society website, "Cancer Facts & Figures 2003,": http://www.cancer.org/docroot/STT/stt_0.asp.

Figure 11.22: Adapted from an illustration by William McGinnis, UCSD.

Figure 13.27: Adapted from A. C. Allison, "Abnormal Hemoglobin and Erythrovute Enzyme-Deficiency Traits," in *Genetic Variation in Human Populations* by G. A. Harrison, ed. (Oxford: Elsevier Science, 1961).

Table 16.1: Adapted from Randy Moore et al., *Botany,* 2nd ed. Dubuque, IA: Brown, 1998. Table 2.2, p. 37.

Figure 17.44: Adapted from an illustration from Laurie Grace, "The Recent African Genesis of Humans," by A. C. Wilson, R. I. Cann, *Scientific American,* 1992:73.

Table 18.1: Data from Centers for Disease Control and Prevention website, "Life table for the total population: United States, 1999," *National Vital Statistics Report,* vol. 50, no. 6 (2002): http://www.cdc.gov/nchs/data/nvsr/nvsr50/50_06_01.pdf.

Table 18.2: Adapted from Pianka, E. R., *Evolutionary Ecology,* 6th ed. (San Francisco, CA: Benjamin Cummings, 2000), p. 186. © 2000 The Benjamin Cummings Publishing Company.

Figure 19.17: Adapted with permission from Edward Farmer, *Science,* vol. 276 (1997): 912. Copyright © 1997 American Association for the Advancement of Science.

Figure 20.6c: From C. E. Likens, et al., "Effects of Forest Cutting and Herbicide Treatment on Nutrient Budgets in the Hubbard Brook Watershed Ecosystem," *Ecological Monographs,* 1966, 50: 22–32. Copyright 1966 The Ecological Society of America. Reprinted by permission.

Figure 20.7: From G. Tyler Miller, *Living in the Environment,* 2nd. ed., p. 87 (Belmont, CA: Wadsworth Publishing, 1979). © 1979 Wadsworth Publishing Company.

Figure 20.11: Data from "Global Warming Trends," by P. D. Jones and T. M. L. Wigley, *Scientific American,* August 1990.

Figure 20.12b: Data from University of Cambridge Centre for Atmospheric Science website http://www.atm.ch.cam.ac.uk .

Figure 22.16: Adapted from Elaine N. Marieb, *Human Anatomy & Physiology,* 5th ed. (San Francisco, CA: Benjamin Cummings, 2001) © 2001 The Benjamin Cummings Publishing Company.

Figure 22.21: Data from U.S. Department of Heath website, "Dietary Guidelines: Aim for Fitness,": http://www.health.gov/dietaryguidelines/dga2000/document/aim.htm.

Figure 23.23: Illustration copyright © Irvng Geis.

Figure 27.6: Adapted from W. M. Becker and D. W. Deamer, *The World of the Cell,* 2nd ed. Figure 20.16 (Redwood City, CA; Benjamin/Cummings, 1991) © 1991 The Benjamin Cummings Publishing Company.